THE
CABRY FAMILY
∽ Railway engineers ∾

by
BRIAN LEWIS
with 66 illustrations

RAILWAY & CANAL HISTORICAL SOCIETY

First published in 1994
by the Railway & Canal Historical Society
Registered office: Fron Fawnog, Hafod Road, Gwernymynydd, Mold, Clwyd CH7 5JS
Registered charity no.256047

ISBN 0 901461 17 2

Designed and typeset by
Malcolm Preskett and Carol Davie
and printed in England by
Hobbs the Printers of Southampton

FRONT COVER
Part of the engineer's drawing for the replacement
for Bridge 52 on the Esk Valley line. *Dunbar Collection, BR York*
Inset: Thomas Cabry and Joseph Cabry (Junior). *Weber family collection*

BACK COVER
The royal train at Castle Howard driven by Thomas Cabry
(see illustration no.16)

Contents

Introduction

N O MATTER how famous the engineer who laid out and supervised the construction of a Victorian railway, replying to a toast at the opening banquet was often his last contribution to its history. With the exception of locomotive superintendents and general managers, the limelight of history seldom fell on the staff whose responsibility it was to develop, promote and run the great man's creation. These men did as much to make the steam railway pre-eminent in land transport as did the great engineers, so let us for a change tell part of their story.

In this book, therefore, I have set out to follow the fortunes of a family of engineers whose association with railways goes right back to the building of the Stockton & Darlington Railway. Whilst they were not amongst the first rank of railway engineers, the Cabrys nevertheless spanned a long and interesting period of railway history. Like George Stephenson, they succeeded in rising from humble beginnings and occupied influential positions both in this country and in Belgium during the 1830s and '40s when railway building was at its height. This influence continued through several generations until late in the nineteenth century.

Thomas Cabry and his brother Henry are the principal figures in this narrative. Although Thomas was somewhat eclipsed in later life by the more dominant personality of Thomas Elliot Harrison, the Engineer-in-Chief of the North Eastern Railway, he nevertheless played an important role in the building and running of the York & North Midland Railway, and before that the Canterbury & Whitstable Railway. He was not a great innovator, but was undoubtedly one of those practical men who could turn his hand to almost anything in the period before specialisation. When Thomas was a young man, an engineer's responsi-

bilities included civil engineering as well as locomotives and other rolling stock. Mechanical engineering was only recognised as a separate profession in 1847 with the formation of the Institution of Mechanical Engineers and many of the problems encountered in the early days, some of which are highlighted in this book, showed the need for such specialisation. In his later years Thomas Cabry joined the growing ranks of professional managers that emerged with the spread of the railways. He seems to have had a natural ability to grasp the new technology and was a steady, dependable survivor at the level of management he reached and ably occupied for many years.

Henry Cabry rose to a high position on the Belgian railways, and, like Thomas in England, was a key figure in the running of the first railways in that country. Unfortunately, little is known about Henry's later life so, inevitably, Thomas Cabry's story occupies a large part of this account. Judging by his early brushes with the management of the Leicester & Swannington Railway, and the style of surviving correspondence, Henry Cabry was probably more assertive than his brother and no doubt his advancement up the social scale by marriage would have reinforced any such trait.

Both were protégés of George Stephenson and whilst researching this book it has been brought home to me just how great was the Stephenson sphere of influence. One can scarcely read an obituary or memoir of a Victorian railway engineer without discovering that he either started his career as an apprentice at the Newcastle factory of Robert Stephenson & Co. or was at one time or another an associate of George or Robert Stephenson. The Stephenson system of patronage, from the earliest days at Killingworth Colliery, continued right through to the middle of the nineteenth century and, like Stephenson, Thomas Cabry frequently gave preference to the appointment of men from his home territory in the North East and not least to members of his own family.

The earliest Cabry who has been traced was married in 1738 and was named Joseph, a favourite name with the family who continued to use it through five generations. Our story really begins with his grandson, also Joseph, who was born in Tanfield, County Durham, in 1772. In 1798 he married Mary Wright and they had six children, including Thomas, Joseph and Henry. All three worked in the mines in Northumberland with their father from an early age prior to the family's move to the Wirral around 1819, and where they were well-established by the early 1820s. Whilst Thomas and Henry became railway engineers, Joseph remained in mining, later becoming an innkeeper and smallholder at Ness on the west coast of the Wirral. Although the Cabry name has died out, there are a number of surviving relatives to be found at various places on the peninsula.

All four of Joseph's sons became railwaymen. A more comprehensive family tree can be found at the end of this book but, to put the various members of the family in perspective, and also to clarify the repetition of Christian names occurring in succeeding generations, FIG.1 gives the members of the Cabry family principally involved.

Apart from genealogical details, very little is known of the early history of the Cabry family prior to the birth of Joseph in 1772. However, one rather intriguing legend has been passed down. Several descendants of the family have referred to a long-standing story telling of a connection with the Earl of Derwent. The details are somewhat confused, not least because the Earl was not born until 1829. He was a director of the North Eastern Railway from 1864 to 1888, but only received his title in 1881 when the Earldom was newly created for him, whereas the genesis of the family legend is much earlier. It appears to refer to James Radclyffe, third Earl of Derwentwater, a roman catholic who took part in the Jacobite Rising of 1715 and who was captured after the defeat at Preston. He was found guilty of high treason and beheaded on Tower Hill in the following February.

The Derwentwater family seat was at Dilston, near Hexham in Northumberland. The Hexham Roman Catholic Church registers show that Joseph Cabry married Mary Ratclif on 9 January 1738/9 and that their son, also Joseph, was baptised on 16 July 1739. One of the sponsors was Charles Busby who was for many years a house steward at Dilston under the Derwentwaters. The first Joseph Cabry appearing on the family chart was the son of Thomas Cabry, who it seems likely was a brother of the Joseph that was baptised in 1739. Although this probably provides the connection back to the Derwentwaters, the Cabrys appear to have been humble artisans at this time and the precise relationship, if any, of Mary Ratclif to the Earl is not clear.

Photographs of members of the Cabry family have been hard to find although several have kindly been provided by descendants of Henry Cabry in Brussels. These included the only surviving likeness of Thomas Cabry which may well have been taken at the time of his election as Sheriff of York as the photographer, S. Hoggard of 27 Davygate, York, was in business at that address only from about December 1858 until September 1862.[1]

The spelling of the name

THOMAS Summerside in his *Anecdotes*[2] gives CABERY, but CABRY and CABREY are used fairly indiscriminately in contemporary sources. Thomas, Henry and Joseph Cabry all signed their names with the shorter form of CABRY and, except when quoting, I have used this version throughout. The spelling CAVERY also appears in the Tanfield Parish Registers, for Thomas Cabry's father Joseph, possibly due to the name being misheard by the priest involved, and corroborative evidence that his real name was CABRY comes from family records.

The origin of the name

THE name Cabry appears to be of Celtic origin and was spelt CAIRBRIE (pronounced CARBERY).[3] The name is very rare in Great Britain, which has greatly assisted in genealogical research, but is rather more common in the United States of America. However from enquiries made of dozens of Cabrys, mainly from the Philadelphia area, it seems that they are descended from a completely different branch of the family which emigrated to the States from Ireland in the nineteenth century. There is also a Cabry family related to the American branch living in Sheffield.

Joseph Cabry
1772–1858
Mining engineer

Thomas Cabry
1801–1873
Engineer, York & North Midland
Railway, and later Engineer,
Southern Division of the
North Eastern Railway

Joseph Cabry
1803–1880
Mining engineer and farmer

Henry Cabry
1805–1881
Chief Superintendent
of the Eastern lines, and later
Inspector-General, Belgian
State Railways

Joseph Cabry
*c.*1831–1897
Held various railway
appointments. Finally
Engineer, Central Division,
NER

Henry Cabry
*c.*1833–1871
Traffic Manager,
Blythe & Tyne Railway

Charles Cabry
*c.*1835–1900
Succeeded Thomas Cabry
as Engineer, Southern
Division, NER

Thomas Cabry
*c.*1842–1882
NER employee

1. Principal members of the Cabry family of railway engineers

Acknowledgments

From genealogical research I soon found that there were no surviving descendants of the Cabry family readily traceable as the name had died out and so had several branches of families into which Cabry daughters had married. I had almost given up this line of enquiry when a chance advertisement for the reprint of a book written about the first twenty-five years of the Belgian railways put me in touch with Professor A. Lederer of Louvain University in Belgium and through him with the Weber family in Brussels who are descendants of Henry Cabry, who emigrated there in 1835. The Webers have been most helpful in supplying information and a number of early photographs of the Cabry family, some of which are reproduced in this book.

As a number of Cabrys are buried at Neston and elsewhere on the Wirral, I naturally investigated several churchyards and quite by accident noticed the name 'Cabry' as the middle name of a lady called Barbara Francis, buried at Willaston. This chance find led me to Mrs Francis of Willaston and her relative Mrs Head of Thetford. Both these ladies have supplied information which has greatly helped me to build up the missing parts of the Cabry family tree.

I would also like to offer my sincere thanks to the staff of the Public Record Office at Kew who got to know me quite well over a long period and were always most willing to assist and to the National Railway Museum at York for some of the photographs from their large collection. My thanks also to Mr Hugh Murray of York for much help on York family history matters, Mr R. N. Clements of Celbridge, the leading expert on the Midland Great Western Railway of Ireland, and to the late Mr Ken Hoole for the loan of papers concerning early York & North Midland Railway locomotives. Mr S. G. Morrison, the Librarian of the Institution of Mechanical Engineers, has gladly made the facilities of his library available to me on several occasions and the late Mr M. F. Barbey of York supplied valuable information regarding the Wharfe Bridge at Ulleskelf. I have also received much help on civil engineering matters, and bridges in particular, from Mr S. Tyson, also of York. Mr Malcolm Scott of the British Rail Bridge Office at York has also been most helpful with regard to the bridges on the Grosmont to Whitby line. Rodney Weaver has been of particular assistance with much helpful advice and information on the technical aspects of valve gears in general, and much of the assessment of early valve gears in Chapter 8 is based on his notes. In addition he has kindly provided the technical assessment of Henry Cabry's valve gear and brake carriage. Grahame Boyes and Malcolm Preskett have spent many hours assisting with the finalising of the text and production of this book and several other Society members have made a number of helpful suggestions and observations. Richard Dean has kindly drawn the maps from my rough drafts and my friends David Robinson and Michael Bundy gave valuable help and advice in the early stages of preparation of this book.

I would also like to acknowledge the assistance given to me by:

The British Library
The Canterbury Cathedral Archive and
    Library, Canterbury
The Leicester Museum of Technology
The Royal Belgian Archives, Brussels
The Science Museum Library
York County Libraries
York Minster Library

With regard to Henry Cabry, it has not been possible to trace his long career with the Belgian State Railways in any detail as many early Belgian railway records were lost during two world wars.

CHAPTER ONE

Family Origins

JOSEPH CABRY (senior) was born at Tanfield, County Durham, on 21 June 1772. Little is known about his early life but he married and raised three sons, Thomas, Joseph and Henry, in addition to three daughters. He was a mining engineer and, as each of his sons was baptised in a different parish in the Newcastle area, it would seem that he moved from one job to another fairly frequently at the time. A revealing glimpse of the Cabry family in those far-off days comes to us through the reminiscences of Thomas Summerside, a fellow worker at Killingworth Colliery where Joseph and his three sons were employed at the 'Jimmy' pit.

At the inside working of the engine was Joseph Cabery, senior; and, as fireman, Joseph Cabery, junior; at the drum outside which drew up the laden 'rolleys' and lowered the empty ones, was Henry; at the bank head to hang on and unhook them, Thomas Cabery was employed.[1]

Summerside must have been much the same age as the Cabry youngsters and would have worked with them at Killingworth during the second decade of the nineteenth century.

It was probably at Killingworth that the Cabry family first came into contact with George Stephenson. Stephenson had obtained employment as a brakesman there in 1804 and in 1812 was appointed engine wright. Apparently he had so impressed the colliery owners, a powerful commercial partnership known as the Grand Allies,[2] with his mechanical skill that he was put in charge of all the machinery at their various collieries. In his well-known biography of George and Robert Stephenson,[3] L. T. C. Rolt seems to suggest 1805 as

a date for Summerside's description of the Cabry family at work, but as Henry Cabry was born in that year and his brother Thomas would only have been four the time must have been later. In all probability it was after 1812, when Stephenson was put in charge of the engines at Killingworth, but before 1819 when he wrote to Joseph Cabry senior telling him of a recent fire in the 'Geordie' flue.[4] The 'Jimmy' and 'Geordie' pits were named after Stephenson and one of his brothers. In a letter addressed to Joseph Cabry at Ness Colliery, Parkgate in Cheshire, George Stephenson makes it plain that Thomas was also with Joseph at Parkgate in 1819, leaving his mother and the rest of the family in Northumberland, as the following extract shows:

I have talked a good deal to Mr Johnson about Thomas Wages I hope Sir Thomas will not Behave so mean as you mention in your letter... I think if you can possibly finish the Lifting Engine it will be better – I hope they will lay meanness aside – I will provide work for you and Thomas when you return – I intend setting you both with my brother Robert to assist in erecting the large engine at Tyne Main Colliery.[5]

There is also a postscript added by Robert Stephenson addressed to Thomas Cabry welcoming the news of his recovery from a recent illness and hoping to see him back at Killingworth. The 'meanness' referred to above could therefore have been concerned with payment of Thomas's wages when he was ill. It seems fairly clear from the foregoing that Joseph Cabry and his son had been sent by Stephenson to install an engine at Ness Colliery. Johnson, as well as being principal agent to Sir Thomas Stanley, the mine owner, also owned pits in Northumberland[6] and was obviously well known to George Stephenson, which provides the otherwise rather tenuous connection between Killingworth and Ness. Despite Stephenson's assurance of work when father and son returned to the North, and another similar suggestion in a letter in March 1820,[7] Joseph Cabry stayed in Cheshire and was in due time joined by his wife and family, with the exception of Henry who appears to have remained at Killingworth. Stephenson's earliest letters to Joseph Cabry were addressed care of the local inn and later to Ness Colliery but by 1828 Cabry was paying Land Tax on a house and about three acres of land by the Dee near to the colliery.[8] The letter of March 1820 suggested that Cabry was still having trouble with his employer and tells of a possible visit to Ness by Stephenson.

Mr. Johnson desires me to inform you we are coming in a fortnight or three weeks – It is very likely your Wife will pay you a Visit… If time does not allow me to accompany Mr. Johnson to Ness, you will please let me know your intentions about *coming back* – as I either intend you to go to Burraton or Tyne Main…

Stephenson also refers to Joseph (junior): 'I had him 3 weeks at Chester Engine assisting Robert in making the joints – I have him now at Walker making Soda for Mr. Losh & Co.'

Coal had been mined on the Wirral since about 1760 when the Stanley family of Hooton opened Denhill Colliery near Ness. The coal was not of very good quality and, being for the most part under the estuary of the river Dee, was not easy to extract but the proximity of water transport and markets in Ireland, Wales and the Isle of Man made mining at Ness a viable proposition. In the early days of the mine there were two underground canals, one at about 180 feet down and the other deeper at 282 feet below the surface. These canals extended about a mile out under the Dee and the coal was brought to the bottom of the shaft by barges which were 'walked' along very slowly by men who lay on planks in a similar way to that used in tunnels on the canal system at various places in England.[9] In the newer pits that replaced the original workings in the nineteenth century rails were laid and pit ponies were used until 1916 when machinery was employed – the last pit in the area closed in 1928.

With the experience he gained in Northumberland it seems likely that Joseph Cabry stayed on in charge of the pumping machinery and lifting gear as the mine required constant pumping to counteract seepage of water from the river Dee far above. In 1821 he and two of his sons (presumably the rest of his family had by then joined him) were involved in a dispute between mine owners. This led to some dubious behaviour underground by their employer, Sir Thomas Stanley, regarding boundaries between the canals. Joseph Cabry and his sons had assisted in the erection of boards around the head of their employer's pit to conceal the arrival of building materials which Stanley was using to seal off one of the canals after a court case had gone against him. The whole story was reported at length in the local paper,[10] which included a brief description of the Cabrys part in the affair.

Joseph Cabry (junior) was destined to stay on the Wirral for the rest of his life, first as an engineer and later as a publican and farmer – by 1829 he was landlord of the Wheatsheaf Inn at Ness.[11] When Stephenson was surveying the Liverpool & Manchester Railway in 1824 he asked his father if he could spare Joseph to assist in the survey.[12] It also has been suggested that Joseph was later employed on the construction of the Canterbury & Whitstable Railway[13] but no evidence has been found that he worked on either of these lines. Thomas, however, did not stay long on the Wirral but soon returned to the north and with his brother Henry joined the newly-formed firm of Robert Stephenson & Co. late in 1823. This partnership had been formed in June of that year and engineering and craft apprentices were taken on from October.[14]

Many nineteenth-century railway engineers received their early training from either George Stephenson or his son Robert. The total number must certainly have run into dozens and George in particular was intensely proud of this fact. He seldom missed an opportunity to refer to his influence when speaking at official functions such as the opening of a new line with which he had been associated. For instance, at the dinner following the partial opening of the York & North Midland Railway on 29 May 1839 he was reported as saying:

He was aware he had received assistance, and particularly from young men brought up from his manufactory; but whenever talent showed itself, whether by poor or rich, he had always given it encouragement; and he would venture to say that he had been the means of putting more young men into comfortable positions than any man that had ever lived.[15]

Some of these young men had started as craft apprentices at the Forth Street Works of Robert Stephenson & Co. whilst others became personal assistants to either George or Robert Stephenson.

As late as 1825 George Stephenson was still trying to persuade Joseph Cabry and his family to return to the Newcastle area which he said would '…please your sons for it would get you all together…'[16] In the same letter Stephenson offered him a supervisory job in the company's works, although he acknowledged he might have to accept a drop in pay: '…there is nothing to stop you but wages and I am shore when you get older you would have a gretter desire to be with your sons…'

However, Joseph obviously valued his position at Ness, where he and the remainder of his family were well established, as he did not take up Stephenson's offer.

2. A photograph of Thomas Cabry taken in York by S. Hoggard of 27 Davygate between December 1858
and September 1862 – possibly taken on his election as Sheriff of York in November 1860.
Weber family collection

CHAPTER TWO

Thomas Cabry's Early Years

THOMAS was the eldest of Joseph Cabry's sons. He was born at New York near Newcastle on 6 June 1801 and was therefore in his early twenties when he joined Robert Stephenson & Co.

In endeavouring to follow his progress with the firm and assess his contribution it is necessary to study in some detail the initial orders they received and the appearance of his name in the Company's records.[1]

Shortly after the inception of the firm, and in order to make themselves and their business more widely known, the Stephensons undertook a tour which included visits to London, Bristol, Dublin and Cork. In London they met Christopher Magnay, the retiring Lord Mayor of London, who ran a wholesale stationery concern in the city with his two sons. This firm leased several mills which provided paper for its business, one such mill being at Dripsey in County Cork where earlier in the year a labour dispute had caused some damage. The Stephensons spent most of September 1823 in Cork estimating for a new boiler and force pumps for the mill, as a result of which they gained the order.[2] Thomas Cabry may have assisted in the subsequent installation of this machinery as we know he installed engines in Ireland[3] and this is the only Irish order mentioned in Robert Stephenson & Co.'s records whilst he was working for them. By late 1824 he was certainly working on the Stockton & Darlington Railway[4] assisting in the installation of the stationary engines at Brusselton and Etherley. The two boilers for the Brusselton engine were delivered on site by the end of September 1824[5] and

the one for Etherley at the same time, although work on the erection of the latter engine did not begin until around January 1825. The two engines were completed in about July 1825 and September 1825 respectively.[6]

Thomas Longridge Gooch, brother of Daniel Gooch of Great Western Railway fame and another of Robert Stephenson & Co.'s early apprentices,[7] was also employed on erecting and finishing the Brusselton engine (and possibly the Etherley engine also) from June 1825 until 26 September 1825 after which he left for Stockton where he spent two days at the opening celebrations of the S&DR before returning to Newcastle.[8] He tells us in his diary that the Brusselton engine was first tried on 23 August 1825 and on 4 September, with George Stephenson present, 'they got the ropes laid and pulled wagons up the banks'.

In the autumn of 1826 the head foreman at the Newcastle works left the company and was succeeded by Thomas Cabry who had by then gained much experience in his frequent travels to supervise engine fitting at the premises of various customers. It is known that George Stephenson thought highly of him as he had written to Thomas's father Joseph in 1824: 'Your son Thomas has the appearance of being a very clever man, I shall take care to see him put forward'.[9]

In the meantime, the opening of the S&DR caused great interest. A number of inventors were anxious to offer suggestions to the directors and some were allowed to try out their ideas on the line. One of these was Thomas Shaw Brandreth, a barrister from Liverpool who was later to be one of the contestants in the Rainhill locomotive trials of 1829. He spent some time experimenting with his 'Friction Waggons' which were an early attempt at reducing the friction of the axles 'by the introduction of anti-friction rollers, variously disposed, the design being to convert the rubbing, or sliding, into a rolling action'.[10] Brandreth patented his device on 8 November 1825 and ordered various components from Robert Stephenson & Co., a charge being made to him for 'T Cabrey's time in Darlington fitting [one friction sleeve] per day 3/6d. – 18.0d.'[11] At least one of these wagons was ready for trials by September 1826 and was proved superior to older wagons in a test on 11 September.

Brandreth continued his experiments for some time and further orders were received by Robert Stephenson & Co.[12] However, use of the wagons was discontinued after a time 'and the ingenious principle had to await the invention of roller bearings to be justified'.[13]

Thomas Cabry next appears in the Newcastle firm's records assisting in the erection of a 10 h.p. stationary engine on the Daubhill incline of the Bolton & Leigh Railway in Lancashire.[14] Work here commenced around May 1827 and was completed in November of that year although the railway did not open until 1 August 1828. However Cabry evidently did not stay on the Bolton & Leigh (whose resident engineer, incidentally, was Thomas Gooch) during the whole period of erection of the Daubhill engine. Summerside tells us[15] that Cabry and John Stephenson (one of George Stephenson's brothers) moved the engine from the 'Bobby' pit at the West Moor Colliery at Killingworth, which was by then worked out, to the Longton, Staffordshire, works owned by William Hanbury Sparrow of Wolverhampton, and put it into the pit 'for the same purpose'. Sparrow was an iron founder with seven blast furnaces at Bilston and one at Lane End producing 300 tons of pig iron and 200 tons of bar iron per week, in addition to his activities at Longton.[16] He also supplied pig iron to Robert Stephenson & Co. on at least one occasion.[17] Following an order from Sparrow a 25 h.p. engine (except for fly-wheel and boiler) was commenced in or about July 1827 and completed in December 1827 so it would appear

that Thomas Cabry spent some of this time at Longton.

In the following year, a high pressure engine of approximately 8 h.p. was supplied to T. & E. Brockbank who were reimbursed for Thomas Cabry's expenses in Carlisle during installation of the engine in December 1828.[18] During the first nine months of 1829 a paper machine and two hydraulic presses were supplied to John Annandale & Sons at their Shotley Mill at Consett. Cabry, assisted by a team of five fitters, spent nearly two months at the mill installing the equipment.[19]

Despite the detailed information contained in the Robert Stephenson & Co. records covering Cabry's time in their employ, it has not been possible to ascertain which other installations he might have worked on. However, he was next put in charge of erecting the stationary engines on the Canterbury & Whitstable Railway, of which George Stephenson was the engineer, and from this time on we enter a more fully documented period of Cabry's career.

Canterbury & Whitstable interlude

THE C&WR was first proposed in 1822 and its Act received the Royal Assent on 10 June 1825. However owing to financial difficulties, work had to be suspended more than once whilst further Acts were obtained to enable additional capital to be raised. A harbour at Whitstable, proposed in 1828, was necessary to the overall plan for the railway which had been conceived partly to provide a new route for goods to Canterbury. Until that time the river Stour had been used but this had gradually silted up. Although it had been hoped that the harbour would open at the same time as the railway, for financial reasons construction was not completed until 1832.

Although the exact date of Thomas Cabry's arrival on the C&WR is not known, the Robert Stephenson & Co. records show that his travelling expenses to Canterbury were advanced to him on 11 July 1829.[20] Upon his arrival he was immediately given charge of erecting the two stationary engines on the line, at Clowes Wood and Tyler's Hill.[21] The first of these, for the Tyler's Hill Incline, had been ordered from Robert Stephenson & Co. and was delivered from Newcastle on 20 June 1829[22] so it would seem that Cabry left Newcastle for Canterbury very soon after despatch of the Tyler's Hill engine. The Clowes Wood engine was not sent from Newcastle until November 1829.

Upon the opening of the line on 3 May 1830 Thomas Cabry became the resident engineer, although his appointment is not recorded in the company's minutes. However, as he was already working on the line, the appointment was probably something of a formality. On 7 July 1831 it was suggested by the directors of the railway[23] that a general manager should be appointed and an advertisement was placed in the *Kent Herald* on 28 July 1831.[24] There were 45 applicants, including Cabry and Joshua Richardson who had been resident engineer during the construction of the line and had also been connected with the abortive Blaydon & Gateshead Railway scheme. These two were amongst seven applicants who were short-listed and Richardson gained the post[25] for a period of one year from 29 September 1831 at a salary of £200 a year,[26] with Cabry continuing as engineer. Various entries in the minute book of the company suggest that, from the opening of the line until the appointment of Richardson, Cabry undertook at least some of the duties afterwards carried out by the manager but he was compensated for any loss of responsibility after Richardson's arrival by his appointment on 20 February 1832 as superintendent of Whitstable harbour, which was formally opened on 19 March 1832, albeit without any increase in his annual salary of £150.

As early as the summer of 1831 problems were experienced with the bridge over Church Street, Whitstable, and its dangerous state was brought to the notice of the directors on 18 August.[27] Three plans by E. P. Fordham, the engineer in charge of the construction of the harbour, were considered on 5 September together with two plans by Thomas Cabry who maintained that, by using the company's own workmen, he could rebuild the bridge more economically, particularly by adopting the second of his two plans to replace the upper brickwork with four cast-iron pillars. Although the directors resolved to adopt this plan, nothing seems to have been done at the time, nor was the matter referred to again in the minutes. However,

although it has been suggested[28] that the plans of Thomas Cabry were eventually adopted, it does not seem that cast iron was ever in fact used for the superstructure, as at the time of its demolition in May 1969,[29] the bridge, which was stated to be in its original condition, was of brick construction, so any work by Cabry must have been of a purely remedial nature. It is perhaps surprising that the matter was left in abeyance for several years after the report of its dangerous state in 1831 but Cabry did in fact refer to it in his evidence before the House of Lords Committee on the Great Western Railway Bill in June 1835.

During its committee stages one of the controversial aspects of this Bill was the proposed gradient of 1 in 100 through the Box tunnel. As the Canterbury & Whitstable had attracted a certain amount of attention in view of its relatively steep inclines, Brunel visited the line on 25 May 1835 and conducted tests during three trips on the line. He was particularly interested in the fall of 1 in 56 through the tunnel near Canterbury and went down this stretch twice without the rope from the stationary engine being attached so that sole reliance could be placed upon the brake on the carriage which was allowed to run unchecked but was still stopped within 60 yards.[30] As engineer of the C&WR, Cabry was called to give evidence before the committee on 29 June 1835 largely to dismiss fears that the incline through the Box tunnel would be dangerous to passengers. As part of his attempt to discredit the C&WR as a badly-built line with dangerously steep gradients, the cross-examining counsel raised the subject of the defective bridge at Whitstable. It emerged that the walls of the bridge were bulging and some earth had been removed from behind the brickwork to lessen the load. Cabry confirmed that the railway was as a result being carried on planks, and that the bridge had been in that state for at least two years. In his summing up, the Hon. J. C. Talbot, the leading counsel for the promoters of the Bill, gently ribbed his opponents.

Then my learned friends on the other side – and I was surprised that they thought it worth while – cross-examined this gentleman and Mr. Stephenson as to the construction of the railroad, and they succeeded in proving there was a bulging bridge likely to fall down by and by; and all I can say is, if there is a bulging

3. A contemporary engraving showing the locomotive *Invicta* leaving Whitstable on the opening day of the Canterbury & Whitstable Railway on 3 May 1830. *Author's collection*

bridge, so much more reason for the passengers to be alarmed, – but they are not alarmed, they travel without apprehension.

The C&WR had experienced continuing financial difficulties. The cost of construction had been under-estimated and even after the line was opened to traffic the difficulties continued and the makeshift repairs to the Whitstable bridge may well have been the result of financial constraints.

When the line was converted for locomotive haulage throughout in 1846 as part of the South Eastern Railway, Major General Pasley, the Board of Trade inspector, said the bridge:

…is one of the original Bridges built of brick at an angle of about 50 degrees but not according to the approved form for skew bridges, all the joints of the arch being parallel to the abutment walls so that properly speaking the arch at each end has only one abutment. Doubting the strength of this construction, strong woodwork has been introduced longitudinally to relieve the arch from the weight of passing trains.[31]

In July 1831 the contract was let for construction of the harbour at Whitstable and in the following month Cabry was instructed to lay tracks on the sea wall as fast as it was completed. At the board meeting of 6 February 1832 it was resolved that four additional cranes to Cabry's design should be procured and that he should proceed to Chatham and London to obtain the necessary ironwork. One of Cabry's duties as harbour superintendent was the collection of rates for vessels entering the harbour and, being unsure of what rates to charge, the directors sent him to Margate, Ramsgate and Dover to discover current practice and methods of collection. Cabry reported back in time for the next board meeting and Richardson was asked to examine the results and draw up a schedule for consideration. It would seem that the silting up, which was to cause problems in the years ahead, had begun to make its presence felt fairly soon after the opening, as Cabry made two reports in June 1832 resulting in an order to him to make a flood gate. The directors also ordered a 'Mid-mud Barge' for use in the harbour.[32] At the board meeting on 30 July, Cabry was ordered to purchase two barge-loads of rag-stone to secure the pier head and also to employ sufficient men to finish the pilings of the harbour and filling up the bed of the wall.

Towards the end of 1831 it had become apparent that the company's only locomotive, the *Invicta,* was not performing satisfactorily on the Church Street Incline at Whitstable, so Richardson was instructed to obtain estimates for an engine house and associated works in order that a third stationary engine could be introduced on the line to solve this problem. This left only the short distance of just over a mile of level track for locomotive haulage, from the top of the Church Street Incline to Bogs-hole Brook where the next incline, operated by the stationary engine at Clowes Wood, commenced.

In August 1835[33] Cabry produced a plan for keeping the harbour clear of silt with the aid of the *Invicta,* which was presumably to provide the power for some form of scouring equipment. Cabry estimated the cost of this exercise at £100 and the C&WR directors resolved to try his scheme in the ensuing autumn and winter, instead of incurring the greater expense of building a 'reservoir for back water'. There is no further reference to this matter in the company minutes so it is uncertain whether the *Invicta* was in fact used in this way.

Invicta was still at work on the level section of the line in 1835[34] so, if it was in fact used to assist in dredging the harbour at Whitstable, it must have been adapted in such a way that it could still be used as a locomotive when not employed on these duties. In early 1836[35] Cabry produced a plan for providing the *Invicta* with a single iron flue in place of the copper tubes in the multi-tubular boiler. This was a seemingly retrograde step which can only be explained in terms of a saving of cost and he may have done the work himself using knowledge gained when he was with Robert Stephenson & Co., prior to the invention of the multi-tubular boiler. Unfortunately Cabry's work did not improve matters and the locomotive, which until then had merely been inadequate, now became totally useless and its use probably ceased forthwith. This is supported by Major General Pasley who said, in his report of 1846 (mentioned earlier), that about ten years previously most of the line was operated by stationary engines but the remainder was worked by horses.[36] The locomotive was offered for sale in September 1839[37] but there were no takers, so the engine languished under cover until the South Eastern Railway took the line over in 1846. It was then moved to the company's Ashford Works and was eventually put on display at Canterbury.

The somewhat ill-defined division of responsibility between manager and engineer apparent earlier can again be seen in operation here, as Richardson arranged for the erection of the third engine house and ordered the sheaves and new rope, whereas Cabry provided a plan for the new stationary engine itself.[38] It was to be a 15 h.p. high pressure engine with two tubes in the boiler[39] and was ordered from Robert Stephenson & Co. to be delivered in parts as soon as they were ready. Presumably, therefore, erection of the engine was under the supervision of Cabry, who reported completion of the engine to the directors on 27 August 1832. Three years later Cabry suggested improvements to the Clowes Wood and Tyler's Hill engines, aimed at an annual saving in fuel costs of £300 for an initial outlay of £700.[40]

Although he produced a plan and estimate in 1835 this work had still not been commenced by the time he resigned his position in July 1836 in favour of a more challenging post in Yorkshire.[41] He was still a young man and plainly had something of a dead-end job on the Canterbury & Whitstable, a small impecunious line facing totally the wrong way to allow any extension, especially in the direction of London. After his resignation however it would seem that work was started on the improvements to the stationary engines, as the directors expressed the hope that 'Mr Cabry may, as far as his stay will allow, superintend the alteration and leave instructions for its completion'.[42] In fact Cabry had previously 'received an advantageous offer of a situation in America'[43] early in 1834 and got as far as tendering his resignation from 1 May of that year but was induced to remain in Canterbury by an increase of salary from £150 to £200.[44]

CHAPTER THREE

Opportunity and Advancement on the York & North Midland Railway

EVERAL SCHEMES for connecting north east England with London had been mooted and a committee had been formed in York in 1833 to consider a railway link with Leeds. Horse power was at first suggested, but in 1835 George Hudson, a member of the committee and later to become known as the Railway King, met George Stephenson in Whitby where the latter was engaged in the construction of the Whitby & Pickering Railway. Both he and his son Robert were in favour of locomotive power and in September 1835 George Stephenson announced his plans for what were to become the North Midland Railway and the Midland Counties Railway which, via Rugby and then over the London & Birmingham Railway, would give a through route from Yorkshire to London. This made the committee realise that the best way to attain their objective of reaching Leeds, and with the added benefit of a through route to the capital, was to build a line to connect with the NMR and also make a junction with the Leeds & Selby Railway at South Milford.

Stephenson and his assistant Frederick Swanwick, who was also supervising work on the W&PR at the time, surveyed the route of the projected York & North Midland Railway south from York to connect with the NMR at Altofts and in due course the Royal Assent was given to the Y&NMR Bill on 21 June 1836. The Whitby & Pickering line was opened throughout in May 1836 and the Y&NMR survey was completed at about the same time. As Swanwick then severed his connection with the line to assist Stephenson with his survey of the NMR, a resident engineer was required to supervise the construction of the Y&NMR.

Thomas Gooch seems to have been Stephenson's original choice as assistant engineer for the construction of the Y&NMR.[1] Gooch, who was some seven years younger than Cabry, had originally intended to take the post of resident engineer on the Manchester & Leeds Railway on condition that he could also assist Stephenson on the York & North Midland. The directors of the M&LR were not happy with that arrangement, so Gooch was induced to devote all his attention to their line and was offered an extra £300 per year plus expenses, which he accepted.[2] This left an opening which Stephenson offered to Thomas Cabry who arrived on the York & North Midland on 21 November 1836.[3] However, Cabry's resignation from the Canterbury & Whitstable Railway nearly two months before it was decided that Gooch would not go to the Y&NMR, and his commencing salary of £500 a year, would seem to suggest that Gooch might have been destined to be an assistant to Stephenson only during the early stages of construction, whereas Cabry had been offered a permanent post with the Y&NMR. Certainly Gooch's duties on the M&LR would have occupied much of his time, and Cabry was also kept very busy from the moment he arrived.

Cabry went to work immediately and by Christmas was able to inform the directors that the line had been staked out as far as Copmanthorpe Field.[4] John Outhett was appointed assistant surveyor and engineer under Cabry from 1 January 1837 with a salary of £200 a year.[5] Construction of the first section of line commenced in April and during the year Cabry staked out the line as far as the junction with the L&SR at South Milford.

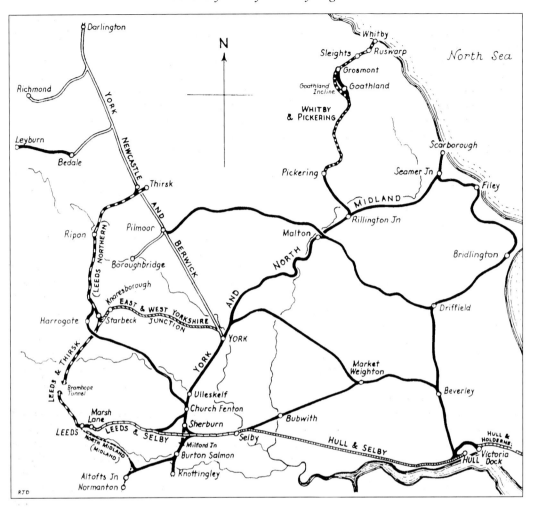

4. The York & North Midland Railway and associated lines, which later formed the Southern Division of the North Eastern Railway, as they developed during Thomas Cabry's working life. The layouts in the main towns have been simplified.

Trouble with several landowners, in particular Lord Howden, led to several deviations from the route approved in the original Act[6] and Cabry was sent to London in June 1837 to give evidence to the House of Commons Committee before the passing of an Act of Amendment on 30 June 1837.[7]

Some idea of the very varied nature of a resident engineer's duties in the early days of railway construction before specialisation had come to the engineering world can be gained from the many matters that Cabry was expected to deal with. These included negotiations with landowners and estimates for contracts, drawing up plans for various bridges and other structures along the line, purchase of rails, engagement of staff (including enginemen), arranging for sleepers to be purchased and Kyanised (an early form of anti-rot treatment patented by Doctor John Howard Kyan in 1832) and the ordering of rolling stock in liaison with Robert Stephenson.

In fact Robert Stephenson took over from his father as Y&NMR Engineer in August 1840[8] but he would have been more involved with the rolling stock at an earlier date as Robert Stephenson & Co. were suppliers of the first locomotives to the company. As time went on his role became that of consultant and for many years the company liked to feel they could call on him as an arbiter in case of difficulty or dispute. Quite how much involvement, if any, Cabry had in locomotive design is hard to say but in March 1839[9] he was instructed to order an engine from Robert Stephenson & Co. 'according to his own plan'. There is however no evidence to suggest that the engines supplied by Stephensons at this time were anything but their standard product, so Cabry probably only influenced comparatively unimportant details.

The design of most of the stations, including the new terminus at York, was carried out by a well-known York architect, George Townsend Andrews, and his plan for breaching the city wall to allow the railway to enter had been adopted in preference to one submitted by Cabry.[10] However Cabry was responsible for a number of minor buildings including the station at Bolton Percy.[11] The last five miles (Contract No.4) from a point near Ulleskelf to the junction with the Leeds & Selby were not let under contract but given to Cabry to supervise directly. The terrain was easy

and the directors hoped to achieve a saving by avoiding employing a contractor for this stretch of the line.[12]

The first section of the line from York to Gascoigne Wood Junction was opened on 29 May 1839.[13] During 1840 various further sections were completed and on 1 July the opening of the connection with the NMR made it possible to travel by rail from London to York for the first time. For a brief period, between the opening of the Hull & Selby Railway on 1 July 1840 and the Y&NMR's Methley branch on 27 July, traffic between Hull and Leeds used the L&SR as did that between York and Leeds, necessitating a change at Milford Junction. The opening of the Methley branch of the Y&NMR gave it a separate route from York to Leeds but one which was four and a half miles longer. Hudson wanted a share of the Hull to Leeds traffic but was concerned at the probable loss of some of the York to Leeds passengers. Having failed to come to a working arrangement with the L&SR he offered to lease the line on terms the directors could not refuse and from 9 November the L&SR was partially closed to passenger traffic forcing all travellers to use the longer route via the Y&NMR and NMR between Milford Junction and Leeds.

Peter Clarke, general manager and superintendent of the L&SR, was retained in that position and also put in charge of the merchandise department of the Y&NMR at an annual salary of £600. Cabry's salary was also raised to the same figure on 5 November from which date he was 'to have entire management of the Engine and Carriage Department and maintenance of roads and bridges on the Leeds and Selby and York and North Midland Railways'.[14] As a consequence of the Y&NMR takeover Cabry and Clarke were immediately instructed to examine costs on the L&SR and reduce them as much as possible[15] in line with the policy of cutting back the competing services. Much was made in the Yorkshire newspapers of an unfortunate accident on 11 November, only two days after the lease became effective, when two passengers were killed at the Y&NMR junction with the L&SR at Milford. This was the first fatal accident involving passengers since the Y&NMR opened and the unfortunate timing gave ammunition to Hudson's critics on the subject of economy versus safety.[16] Cabry gave evidence at some length at the inquest supporting John Watkins, the driver of the goods train which had run into the rear of a standing passenger train. He was a man who had been known to Cabry for 20 years and had been brought down from the North as he was known to be 'an exceedingly steady and intelligent man'.[17]

On 3 June 1841 Thomas Cabry married Margaret Ann Bookless. There is strong circumstantial evidence from genealogical sources to indicate that she was a relative by marriage of George Hudson but it has not been possible to prove this conclusively. However Hudson was certainly one of the witnesses at their wedding at St Stephen's Church, Acomb near York. No doubt Cabry had moved in social circles within the railway hierarchy and it was only natural that he should choose a wife from amongst these acquaintances. Margaret was thirteen years younger than Thomas, then in his 41st year, and the marriage was to be childless. His close relationship with Hudson over the ensuing years would undoubtedly have been fostered by a family tie. Thomas and his bride moved into 26 Blossom Street in York where they lived for three years. The property was purchased by the North Eastern Railway in 1888, becoming the York Station Master's House. It has been occupied by the New York Club (formerly the York Railway Men's Club and Institute) since 1934.[18] In 1844 the Y&NMR purchased some land in Holdgate Lane, adjacent to the railway, and shortly afterwards built a large detached house known as Holdgate (later Holgate) Villa within the railway company's boundary.[19] The York street directories give this as Cabry's address in 1851 so it seems probable that the couple moved into the new house, presumably built specially for them, which was provided rent-free as part of Cabry's salary.[20] They lived at Holgate Villa until 1865 when the house was converted into offices for the engineering department.[21] This property also remained in railway hands and was later lived in by Harold Copperthwaite the NER District Engineer at York from 1888 to 1899.[22] It was demolished after the Second World War to make way for a modern British Railways office block, also known as Holgate Villa.[23]

The North Midland affair

TOWARDS the end of 1842 Cabry's name became linked for the first time with railway politics. The North Midland had been an expensive line to build and traffic receipts had not come up to expectations, resulting in low dividends since its opening in 1840. This brought pressure from a group of shareholders for economies to be made and a Committee of Inquiry was set up in August 1842 of which George Hudson was a member. The committee reported a month later and recommended, amongst other things, a reduction of nearly 50% in Locomotive Department expenses.[24] On 16 November these recommendations were adopted by the proprietors – followed a week later by Hudson's appointment to the board in place of one of several directors who had resigned over the new policies – and it was speedily decided to discharge five engine crews and reduce the wages of the remainder. This action together with other economies was a recipe for chaos, which soon threatened as inexperienced staff grappled with day-to-day operations while the remaining experienced employees whose wages had been reduced were not in co-operative mood. Having already been involved with Swanwick, the NMR resident engineer, in making alterations to pointwork at Normanton which dispensed with two pointsmen,[25] Cabry was called in by Hudson in an effort to minimise disruption to traffic over the Christmas period.[26] Major General Pasley, the Board of Trade inspector sent to investigate the reduction in wages of the NMR enginemen, had visited Derby and Leeds in December 1842, when he met a group of directors and officials, including Cabry, and, although he had initially been satisfied with the new working arrangements, he was later to change his mind.

The company minutes record that on 14 January 1843:

It appearing desirable that some better arrangement for conducting the locomotive business at Leeds and Derby is required and Mr. Hudson having stated that Mr. Cabrey, Resident Engineer of the York and North Midland Railway, had offered to devote some time to the superintendence of that department on this line for a month or two.

and it was resolved:

…that Mr. Cabrey's offer be accepted and that he be

5. The house at 26 Blossom Street, York (now the New York Club) where Thomas Cabry and his wife lived from 1841 to 1844. *Author*

invited to proceed to Derby as early as possible to take the entire charge of the Locomotive Department and that the Secretary be ordered to pay off any servant or servants of the Company which Mr. Cabrey may think it desirable to part with.

It was also resolved that 'no person be appointed to drive an engine unless approved of by Mr. Cabrey';[27] wide powers indeed. The reaction of Marshall, the NMR locomotive superintendent,[28] who had only avoided dismissal in the general shake-up after the intervention of Robert Stephenson,[29] can well be imagined. This provocative action did not go unnoticed in the railway press and an accident on 12 January at Cudworth, involving a collision between a luggage train and a stationary passenger train, brought strong criticism of the company's methods from Pasley in his subsequent report, as it emerged that the driver of the luggage train had had only three weeks' experience on the footplate.

The sternest critic however was 'Veritas Vincit' whose letters to the *Railway Times* and later the *Railway Record* on this and many other mis-demeanours by railway management appeared at

frequent intervals over the next four or five years. The Hudson empire was one of his favourite topics. To put what follows into perspective it should be mentioned that the 1840s were a period of intense interest in railway management and finance by the press and public and several substantial weekly papers, of which the *Railway Times* was only one, were devoted to their progress. 'Veritas Vincit' did not confine his criticisms to Cabry alone as a number of other superintendents also met with his disapproval. Nevertheless the Y&NMR reputedly had the worst carriages at this time and Hudson was certainly preoccupied with expansion and the provision of an attractive dividend for his shareholders. The development of the locomotive was still in an early and imperfect phase and Cabry, along with others, was still coping with the daily difficulties of running a train service. He was probably no less equipped than many other loco-motive superintendents at the time but obviously trod on a number of corns, as will be seen, and received a good deal of attention in the press, little of it favourable. The writings of 'Veritas Vincit' have become acknowledged by railway historians to be

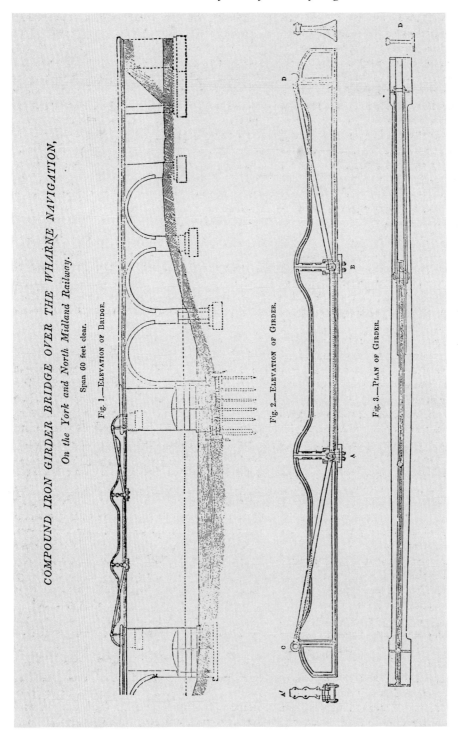

COMPOUND IRON GIRDER BRIDGE OVER THE WHARNE NAVIGATION,

On the York and North Midland Railway.

Span 60 feet clear.

Fig. 1.—Elevation of Bridge.

Fig. 2.—Elevation of Girder.

Fig. 3.—Plan of Girder.

6. The compound iron-girder bridge over the river Wharfe (incorrectly spelt in drawing title !) at Ulleskelf which was rebuilt under Thomas Cabry's supervision in 1843. The construction of the cast-iron beam with the wrought-iron trusses and the clear span over the river that the girders provided can be clearly seen. 'Railway Chronicle'

accurate and, although his identity has never been discovered, he was evidently in a position to observe events at first hand and no doubt kept his ear close to the ground. It has been suggested that the author was John Robertson,[30] editor of the *Railway Times* who founded the *Railway Record* in April 1844 and edited it until he died in the cholera epidemic of 1849 at the early age of 39.[31] Certainly 'Veritas Vincit' changed his allegiance to the new journal when it first appeared. His collected letters were later published[32] and they give us a rare glimpse of the realities of day-to-day management which are virtually unobtainable elsewhere and particularly not in company minute books – the Y&NMR records being particularly scant during this period.

The North Midland affair still rumbled on. The Board of Trade had suggested that the working arrangements were now compromising public safety on the line but the directors disagreed[33] and supported their actions by quoting Cabry's pronouncement that he found the new drivers 'equal in Skill and carefulness to the Men they have replaced'. They supplied evidence that things were much improved and running to their satisfaction. They did however concede longer rest intervals to crews of passenger trains and got rid of the worst of the new intake of enginemen. Having completed the reorganisation of the department, Cabry resigned the charge of the NMR locomotives in March 1843,[34] no doubt to the relief of all concerned, and received fifty guineas for his trouble.[35]

'Veritas Vincit' however was only just beginning. Hudson had tried to justify his actions on the NMR at the half-yearly Y&NMR meeting in February 1843. He had said, in effect, that the new enginemen on the NMR were as good as the old and that high wages did not necessarily buy safety. 'Veritas Vincit' alleged that the new men 'were bred in precisely the same manner as that highly-talented gentleman, Mr. Cabrey, upon whom so much praise is lavished' and alluded darkly to Cabry's methods on his own line and quoted cases of two unsatisfactory drivers engaged by him on the North Midland. During the North Midland affair Hudson had apparently alleged that oatmeal had been put into the locomotive boilers in an attempt to sabotage them. 'Veritas' reminded his readers that this was a well-known remedy for leaking tubes and 'not long ago, before the improvement of the fire-boxes and

ferulling of the tubes, there was scarce ever an engine sent out without having either oatmeal or bran put into the boiler.' He believed horse dung was even better 'and I daresay Mr. Cabrey could tell Mr. Hudson that he has put many a bucketfull of horse dung into a boiler, when he worked the colliery engine in Northumberland'. Hudson had also complained that the NMR engines were in a bad state of repair when the new directors took over, whereas the reverse was true – the damage having been done by the newly engaged and inexperienced drivers. Marshall, the NMR locomotive superintendent, seems to have come out of the affair on the right side, as his salary was increased[36] presumably leaving only injury to his pride.

Major General Pasley kept a diary during the time he was at the Railway Department,[37] and although this does not contain a great deal of information relevant to the present account, he did meet Cabry on a number of occasions and it was Pasley who had to investigate the NMR enginemen's wages mentioned earlier.

The Wharfe Bridge at Ulleskelf

RETURNING to civil engineering matters, one of Cabry's major problems during the building of the Y&NMR was at Ulleskelf where the line from York to Milford crossed the river Wharfe. A brick bridge of nine semi-elliptical arches had originally been planned, the centre arch over the river being of 60 feet span and the four approach arches on each side 15 feet. The lowest tender had been submitted by John Powell of York and he was awarded the contract on 12 October 1837.[38] However the first hint of trouble came later in the same month when Powell asked for the completion time to be extended from ten to twelve months; the board refused[39] and just after Christmas, Cabry was ordered to supervise the erection of the bridge personally.[40] Further delays were caused by bad weather, the nature of the ground and problems with the contractor but the bridge was ready in time for the opening of the railway on 29 May 1839.

The ground on either side of the river, which had caused difficulties during the construction of the bridge, continued to give trouble. Robert Stephenson was requested to make an emergency inspection of the bridge the day before the half-yearly company meeting on 29 January 1841 (as a result of a letter from Sir Frederic Smith to Thomas Cabry regarding the safety of the bridge)[41] although the matter was not raised at the meeting. It is probable that the main arch was failing although not in immediate danger of collapse and early in 1843 it was decided that the centre span of the bridge should be replaced by compound girders. The cast-iron girders, made up of three sections, were trussed for extra strength with underhung wrought-iron rods anchored to their upper extremities. The theory was that by combining the tensile strength of wrought iron with the compressive strength of cast iron a much stronger beam could be achieved than with either material alone. However the mechanical properties of cast and wrought iron differed so much that in practice the cast-iron beam was overstressed long before the wrought-iron truss rods took their fair share of the load. Compound girder bridges enjoyed some popularity in the 1840s but the safety of the design depended on the correct anchoring of the truss rods and a degree of pre-stressing. These theories were not fully understood and whilst some such girders, used for short spans, were merely an unnecessary complication, others were liable to fail at any time. The collapse of a similar structure of 98 feet span over the river Dee at Chester in 1847, which was the longest compound girder span used up to that time, prompted the Railway Inspectorate to call on all railways to submit a return of iron bridges. The use of cast iron remained controversial due to its inherent weakness in tension, although the Y&NMR bridge was not further rebuilt for nearly 40 years.

The tender for the Ulleskelf bridge by John Walker of Rotherham was accepted and in due course he received £791 for the work.[42] Probably to disguise the true reason for rebuilding the central span so soon after completion in brick, the pro-Hudson *Railway Chronicle*[43] reported that the new span was designed by Cabry to give maximum headroom for navigation, and it was also stated that complaints had been received from river users.

The *Railway Chronicle* tells us that Cabry 'opened up the road-way on the back of the arch, he inserted masonry to carry the bearings of the large cast-iron girders, he had these girders erected in their place, without disturbing all this while either the arch below the railway or the rails

themselves'. The lines were dealt with one at a time, the piers being dressed to receive the girders which were then brought to the site on trucks and lowered into place by jacks on beds of lead a quarter of an inch thick. A platform of Memel timber nine inches thick was then placed on the bottom flanges of the beams to carry the track. In this way the railway was in effect carried on two bridges simultaneously, after which 'One fine morning…Mr Cabry chose to knock away the under one'. This rather whimsical description is reminiscent of the well-known story of Brunel's similar action a few years previously when building the extremely flat elliptical arch over the Thames at Maidenhead which no one thought would stand until the centering was blown away in a storm revealing that the bridge had not after all been supported by it for some time. In fact the brickwork of the Wharfe Bridge was removed with the aid of scaffolding suspended from the platform of the new bridge without interrupting rail or river traffic. The site of the Wharfe crossing at Ulleskelf has had a bad reputation due to subsidence ever since and no part of the original structure remains, not even the approach arches which were of small span and would normally have been virtually indestructible. The cast-iron girders were replaced in 1881 by a wrought-iron structure[44] and the present bridge, of welded steel-plate girders, was built in 1955.[45]

Not surprisingly 'Veritas Vincit' had something to say about Cabry's involvement in this enterprise.[46] He pointed out that the original workmanship, under Cabry's supervision, had been faulty and it was therefore necessary to replace the centre span on grounds of safety. He even denied Cabry any credit for the new design which he said was a slight adaptation of a bridge on the London & Blackwall Railway. The *Railway Chronicle*, ever faithful to the Cabry cause, reported the construction of a compound iron-girder bridge over a road on the Leeds & Bradford Railway in 1845 as being based on the Wharfe Bridge design.[47]

Veritas Vincit strikes again

IN August 1843 'Veritas Vincit' launched into Cabry again, this time on the subject of the Leeds & Selby which had been leased by the Y&NMR in 1841. Changes of foremen had been frequent and the drivers were 'inexperienced and strange.' 'Veritas' mentioned various malpractices and said that, even while Hudson was making his speech deploring the use of oatmeal on the North Midland, every driver on the Leeds & Selby carried a bran bag and that inexperienced drivers had used it so much and neglected regular boiler wash-outs that many fireboxes were burned, giving Cabry first-hand experience of the folly of cheap drivers.

Later in August 'Veritas' focussed his attention on the York & North Midland which he said had been 'held up as a paragon of excellence' and went on to list a number of incidents caused by inexperience or carelessness to drive home his point. In September he was back on the subject, suggesting this time that Cabry had 'availed himself of the labour of other men's brains in reference to a so-called invention of his connected with the engine…' It is not made clear what this might have been but he goes on to advise Cabry to look at the locomotive stock on the Hull & Selby under John Gray, the locomotive superintendent, with regard to economical coke consumption. The 'so-called invention' may refer to the trial on the Y&NMR of a valve gear designed by Thomas Cabry's brother Henry, which will be fully described later. Gray had also patented a form of expansion valve gear which was in use on the H&SR at the time.

'Veritas Vincit' did not have things all his own way however as another anonymous correspondent entered the fray in defence of the NMR and Cabry's management methods. Several exchanges took place but the editorial comments make one wonder if some of the correspondence was not stage-managed to give 'Veritas' (the editor also?) further scope for his invective. In September 1843,[48] through the good offices of Sir John Simpson, a director of the Y&NMR, Cabry was once again invited to advise on a supposedly unsatisfactory situation in a locomotive department. This time it was the London & Brighton Railway of which Sir John was also a director. Not unnaturally the Brighton Locomotive Superintendent, Thomas Statham, was hostile to Cabry's findings and 'Veritas' continued to have a great deal to say upon the matter.

Briefly, the facts are these. Statham, basically a civil engineer but probably doing an adequate job with the equipment at his disposal, had been appointed on completion of the Brighton line a few years earlier, having been assistant to John Rastrick, the Brighton company's engineer. By the summer of 1843 the locomotive stock was in poor condition.[49] Rastrick blamed the lack of facilities and recommended that new locomotive and carriage repair shops should be built at Horley. To assist them in coming to a decision the new chairman and several directors were invited by Sir John Simpson to visit the Y&NMR to see Cabry's methods for themselves.[50] Thereafter Cabry examined the stock and submitted a report on 2 October[51] and Statham was ordered to prepare his own report for the directors immediately.[52] Cabry attended a board meeting on 12 October to explain his findings and, at a special meeting on the following day, his report was read to Statham who 'contradicted the allegations contained therein'. Cabry was then called into the meeting and Statham's report was read in the presence of them both. A 'discussion' took place and the reports were ordered to be referred to Mr Edward Bury, or failing him Mr James Kennedy or Mr James Fenton, all of whom were well-known locomotive engineers.[53] At the same meeting Cabry was asked to supply a list of engines he considered unsafe for passenger traffic and Statham was ordered to withdraw them from service until Kennedy, who was chosen as the independent arbitrator, had made his report. In the meantime Kennedy refused to read the conflicting reports as he wished to approach the matter with an open mind. He largely confirmed Cabry's findings and Statham was given three months notice. Statham did not give in without a further fight, however, and offered to reduce the enginemen's wages over a six-month period to bring the cost down to that recommended in Cabry's report.[54] He also promised to reduce maintenance staff levels by mechanisation. Although the directors wavered,[55] saying they would await his detailed proposals, Statham left the company shortly afterwards and was replaced by John Gray from the Hull & Selby Railway.[56] Further parallels with Cabry's intervention on the NMR were drawn by 'Veritas Vincit'[57] as there had apparently been some allegations of corruption regarding appointments and dismissals on the L&BR and certainly men were brought from the north to work in the locomotive department.[58]

Whilst Cabry was in Brighton he was asked to advise on workshop equipment and the condition of the company's other rolling stock, and had also been asked to prepare a plan and estimate for a new joint station with the South Eastern Railway at Reigate (Redhill). This station, which was brought into use in April 1844,[59] was in fact built by the SER which was the company principally interested in a joint station, and it was designed (if that is the right word for it) by Peter William Barlow, an assistant engineer on the SER. The editor of the *Railway Times* (who may also have been 'Veritas Vincit' as mentioned earlier) said that Cabry had had his 'laurels somewhat scathed in the matter', Barlow's plan having been adopted in preference to his.[60] In reality, Cabry was probably only being asked to ensure that the building would be put up as cheaply as possible. The linking of his name with the enterprise however was seen as yet another piece of unwarranted intrusion on his part. Certainly the London & Brighton were somewhat reluctant to have a joint station, perhaps thinking there was more revenue to be had from their own. The new station was hastily erected and was 'a crude affair of wood tarpaulins and iron pillars which somehow did duty for 14 years'.[61] Apparently it was so rotten and decayed by 1858 that it was replaced in August of the following year. The whole episode was seen by some of the *Railway Times'* correspondents as an indication that Hudson was seeking to extend his empire southwards and intended to install Cabry and his men on the Brighton line as a prelude to a full take-over.

The running of the locomotive department of the Y&NMR also came under the eye of 'Veritas' in 1843.[62] Obviously he was an admirer of the ability and methods of Gray, Cabry's opposite number on the Hull & Selby, who was considered by many at the time to be a highly capable and inventive engineer. However, his patent valve gear was cumbersome and surviving drawings of his other work do not support his reputation. The full expansive qualities of steam were beginning to be better understood at this time and Gray had, according to 'Veritas', increased the valve lap on some of his engines. Cabry had apparently copied Gray by adding this improvement to two Y&NMR

engines, *Albert* and *Victoria.* These were conventional 2-2-2 locomotives with 5'6" driving wheels and 12½"x 18" cylinders which had been built by Robert Stephenson & Co. in late 1840. At about the same time Gray designed a 2-2-2 with 6' driving wheels, 13"x 24" cylinders and the high boiler pressure for the period of 90lb per square inch. Six engines built by Shepherd & Todd over a six-month period were fitted with Gray's variable expansion valve gear and in September 1840 Cabry ordered two of these engines – *Antelope* and *Ariel.* Early in 1842 Gray brought out an improved goods engine and 'Veritas' tells us that Cabry again copied the idea by getting one of his staff to measure the engine's principal dimensions and arranging for two to be built by Robert Stephenson & Co., thus giving himself two excellent engines for which he took full credit. He also tells us that it was common knowledge that one H&SR engine could do the work of three Y&NMR engines on heavy goods trains.

Cabry was also accused of tampering with a perfectly sound engine, the *Firefly,* which he had sent to Leeds and 'got her uncoupled and made for a train engine at considerable expense' (this refers to the conversion of a 0-4-2 goods engine to a 2-2-2 passenger type).[63] Some time afterwards the engine was once again expensively returned to its original condition. 'Veritas' suggested that this was done merely to make use of the recently acquired L&SR erecting shops.

This, like the accusation of poaching of ideas, was probably somewhat unkind. It would be only natural for there to be some exchange of information between superintendents of adjacent lines and Gray was paid £150 by the Y&NMR for the use of his patent valve gear on the *Antelope* and the *Ariel,* although not until over a year later.[64] Nevertheless 'Veritas' saw this as further evidence for his low opinion of Cabry. He also deplored the efforts of Cabry in carriage building and itemised a number of instances of poor maintenance and ill-advised alterations to engines made on Cabry's instructions. These details provide information about the Y&NMR locomotive fleet which is unobtainable elsewhere. Needless to say, when Gray left the H&SR to take up his post on the London & Brighton in July 1845, consequent upon the leasing of the H&SR by the Y&NMR, 'Veritas' predicted a decline in the H&SR locomotive stock and was soon able to give a

Two locomotives in use during Thomas Cabry's time on the York & North Midland Railway

7. Y&NMR no.8, originally named *Wellington,* was built in 1840 by Robert Stephenson & Co. (Works no.257) as a 2-2-2 tender engine. It later became NER no.252 and survived until 1894, having been rebuilt as a tank engine. It is seen here attached to an inspection saloon in about 1870. *Ken Hoole collection, by courtesy of the Darlington Railway Centre & Museum*

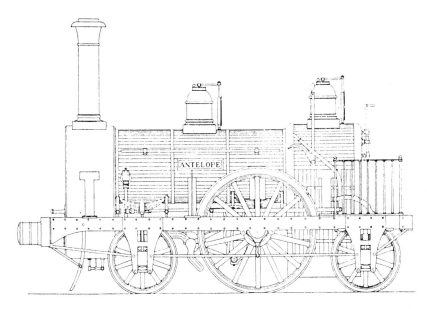

8. Y&NMR no.9 *Antelope* in original condition as fitted with John Gray's valve gear. This locomotive, built by Shepherd & Todd in 1840, was fitted with Stephenson's link motion by 1849. It lasted, in somewhat altered condition with driving wheels reduced from 6' to 5'3", until 1883 in which year the engineer David Joy saw it in the locomotive sheds in York. An identical engine no.10 *Ariel* was also supplied to the Y&NMR and six similar engines, also fitted with Gray's gear, went to the Hull & Selby Railway, but *Antelope* outlasted them all in service. *By courtesy of J. M. Fleming. Prepared from an original sectional drawing*

9. NER no.319, originally Y&NMR no.88 *Jenny Lind*. This famous locomotive was built by E. B. Wilson & Co. in 1847 and was withdrawn in 1879. This photograph is believed to have been taken at Scarborough and shows the engine working the first NER stores train. *Ken Hoole collection, by courtesy of the Darlington Railway Centre & Museum*

number of examples. He was given short shrift when he visited York early in 1846 as his 'last letter had given Mr Cabrey very great offence for the exposure there set forth of his Hull & Selby management.'[65] This, he alleged, was at a time when, but for the arrival of ten new engines from Robert Stephenson & Co., the Y&NMR would have been 'nearly at a stand'.[66] However he managed to collect the information he was after and continued his 'exposure' of Cabry's management methods.

To give him a possible future route into London in the face of competition from the London & York Railway, first promoted in 1844, Hudson had added the impecunious Eastern Counties Railway to his empire and he was simultaneously appointed a director *and* elected Chairman on 14 October 1845.[67] Within a fortnight Fernihough the locomotive superintendent had been given his notice and Thomas Scott, formerly an apprentice of Cabry's and latterly superintendent of the Midland Railway locomotive depot at Leeds, had been appointed.[68] Evidently Cabry was called in to give his customary advice on locomotive matters, as the company minutes record that he was paid one hundred guineas in the following May for his 'recent professional services'.[69] One can readily understand why 'Veritas Vincit' was able to say that Cabry was 'undeniably head locomotive superintendent of all Hudson Lines'.[70] Cabry's protégé did not last long however as Scott was replaced by John Hunter after less than one year.[71] 'Veritas' delivered a parting shot in the direction of Thomas Cabry which appeared in June 1848[72] and concerned the reduction in wages of some drivers on the Y&NMR and also on the York & Newcastle Railway where he had apparently influenced T. E. Harrison, the locomotive superintendent of that line.

CHAPTER FOUR

Expansion on the York & North Midland and the Downfall of George Hudson

ALMOST from the day the line opened the directors of the York & North Midland Railway had nurtured various plans for expansion. An Act for lines to Scarborough and Pickering was obtained on 4 July 1844 and they were opened for traffic on 8 July 1845. Special trains were run on the previous day and Cabry was much to the fore. 'Both on going and returning, the road being 'green', the train under the conduct of Mr Cabrey…was driven with great care…and not the slightest accident happened…'[1] A lavish banquet was held to celebrate the opening and George Stephenson was brought back to deliver his customary eulogy in which he praised Cabry, and others, who 'had been reared up under his own care'.[2] The 'greenness' of the road did cause some problems later however as the 12.15pm train from York came off the rails a quarter of a mile south of Kirkham Abbey station on 25 August owing to subsidence of part of the embankment. Apparently Cabry had been on the engine and had hurt his foot in the process. The incident was minor as the train was travelling very slowly and it was only because a contractor's workman had hidden in the luggage van and been unexpectedly discovered quite badly injured in the wreckage that it had been necessary to report the accident at all.[3] This was not the first landslip on the new line as there had been another north of Kirkham some weeks previously. Both were the result of heavy rain which had caused the river Derwent to burst its banks in the vicinity.

The engineer David Joy wrote down his reminiscences in later life and these give us further glimpses of Cabry and the Y&NMR at this time.[4]

Joy was serving his apprenticeship in Leeds with the locomotive makers Fenton, Murray & Jackson and afterwards with Shepherd & Todd (later to become E. B. Wilson & Co., with whom he stayed until 1850). During this period Shepherd & Todd were building engines for the Y&NMR and the following entries in Joy's diary are of interest:

Autumn 1845 – 'At this time we lads were always on the engines of the Y. & N. Midland Railway (as it was then called) taking little trips to Castleford, Milford and sometimes York. And just now we got an order from this railway for six engines – Thomas Cabry, engineer. I had all these drawings to make.'

May 1846 – 'Long boiler engines were going out; the engines did well, but were bad rollers. One dreary afternoon the driver came, and said Mr. Cabry wished us to see them. Willis and I went, and left with the 4 p.m. express to York, a wet afternoon with driving rain… and did not that engine tumble about. She rolled like a ship in a gale. But we put balance weights on the wheels, and she went all right then, so did all the others when balanced.'

Circa May 1847 – 'Other schemes came to us, one by Thos. Cabry of York chief of the Y&NMR – thus [see figure]. Of course the scheme was not practical, the centres of the cranks were inches out at various points in a revolution… Balancing moving parts was Thos. Cabry's idea…'

An entry of much later date also mentions those days:

1883 – 'On one of these passages through York I strolled through the engine sheds, as in the old days of Thos. Cabry, and saw the old Antelope – a lovely, light, fleet-looking engine still.'

In fact, only four of these long-boiler 2-4-0 engines

were supplied to the Y&NMR by E. B. Wilson & Co., the remaining two being diverted to other Hudson-controlled lines.[5] In view of the overhang at each end, and the outside cylinders, they would have been extremely unstable at speed until properly balanced. Even then the long-boiler type was inherently unsuited to express passenger work and was soon superseded. The 1847 diary entry refers to the balancing of forces by placing the connecting rods on either side of the piston rather than to the principle of balancing of reciprocating parts for which Cabry was certainly not responsible.

Hudson, now at the height of his power and influence, had further schemes in hand. The Hull & Selby Railway had been leased from 1 July 1845 and branches from Hull to Bridlington and from Seamer to Filey were both opened in October 1846. The branch connecting Pickering to the York–Scarborough line served the double purpose of linking Pickering to the railway system and joining up with the Whitby & Pickering Railway. This line, which opened throughout in May 1836, and of which George Stephenson was engineer-in-chief, was originally horse-operated but in 1844 Hudson, who had close links with Whitby and is believed to have had hopes at that time of representing Whitby in Parliament, persuaded the Y&NMR board to make a generous offer to purchase the line and the W&PR (Purchase) Act came into force on 30 June 1845. The railway was rebuilt and opened to locomotives as far as Raindale in August 1846 and throughout on 1 July 1847.[6]

Since the original opening of the horse-worked line a steep gradient had existed between Goathland and Grosmont. It was at first worked by gravity – descending trains were used to haul up ascending ones, with the use of one or more water-filled tanks attached at the top to provide ballast as necessary. Obviously with so steep an incline – it was approximately 1,500 yards long on an average gradient of 1 in 15 – and with the very limited power of locomotives at the time, stationary power had to be retained. When, therefore, the W&PR was rebuilt a stationary engine of 40 h.p. was installed. The engine, which had a winding drum of six feet diameter and a powerful lever brake,[7] was almost certainly built by Charles Todd of Leeds. An entry

in the Y&NMR financial records[8] in July 1846 shows '£200 paid to C. Todd on account of stationary engine' and, although there is no other specific payment mentioned, Todd was supplying locomotives to the company at the time and payments were being made in stages so probably the balance of the money owing for the Goathland engine was hidden in these transactions.

After the Whitby & Pickering line re-opened the incline was worked by special brake vans fitted with a slide or sledge brake. These were similar to those developed by Thomas Cabry's brother Henry for the Liège incline in Belgium, which will be described later. Sledge brakes were considered an attractive alternative to clasp brakes, as at this time it was erroneously believed that the quickest way to stop a train was by locking the wheels. However, this caused excessive vibration and wheel 'flats', and if the wheels did not lock the heat generated by friction could loosen both the tyres and the joints between wheel and axle. To minimise the problem, braking was restricted to vans placed at intervals along the train. Even so, wear and tear and damage to the bearings of these vans brought about a search for a better form of brake. Sledge brakes still suffered from vibration and also, by relieving the wheels of much of their adhesive weight, made the flanges less able to keep the vehicle in line with the rails. Their use was therefore limited to special situations and they never came into general use.

Thomas Cabry's vans were smaller than their Belgian counterparts, having only four wheels and one sledge brake on each side.[9] Also, unlike the Belgian vans, the W&PR vans were probably covered in a similar way to more conventional English brake vans. One of these brake vans was placed near the Goathland summit in readiness and when the train arrived at the top of the incline the engine ran round and pushed its train against the van. The rope from the stationary engine was then attached to the special brake van by a ball-and-socket connection which allowed the rope to be conveyed to the bottom and also controlled the speed of descending trains by means of a brake on the winding drum.[10] After easing the train forward the engine stayed at the top of the incline, leaving it to descend, led by the special brake van with the ordinary train brake van at the rear. As the train

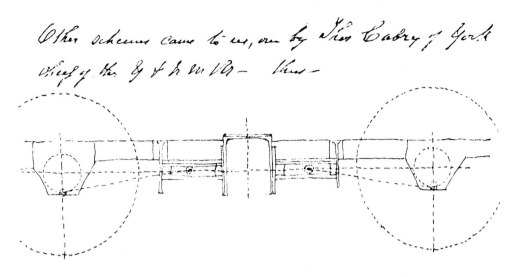

Other schemes came to us, one by Thos Cabry of York chiefly the Eg of h En VDs — thus —

Of course this scheme was not practical, the centres of the cranks were inches out at various points in a revolution

10. Cabry's scheme for a balanced locomotive as illustrated in David Joy's diary *c.*1847.
From an original diary in the Science Museum Library

neared the bottom of the incline the rope was detached from the special brake van by the brakesman whilst the train was still in motion. The brakes of the special van, which was not actually coupled to the following train, were then released to allow it run ahead of the train through a set of facing points into a siding on the right-hand side of the line. The train carried on slowly towards a waiting locomotive which was coupled to it to continue the journey northwards. It seems likely that two of these brake vans were used together for heavier loads and, as will be described later, they were replaced in about 1858 by a larger six-wheeled van.[11]

The Y&NMR also obtained an Act for a branch from Church Fenton, south of York, to Harrogate and this was opened in stages. The first section as far as Spofforth was opened on 10 August 1847 and the remainder on 20 July in the following year. A cross-country line from York to Market Weighton was opened on 4 October 1847 and a further branch from Selby to Market Weighton on 1 August 1848.

It was at this time that Cabry became active in York public life. No doubt through the influence of George Hudson, who was nearing the end of his third term as Lord Mayor of York, Cabry was nominated as a Conservative councillor for the Micklegate Ward, winning the seat on 1 November 1847.[12] He was also amongst the founder members of the newly-formed Institution of Mechanical Engineers in the same year and was for some time a member of the Council of that Institution.[13]

George Hudson's association with the Eastern Counties Railway was to be short-lived as he was obliged to resign his directorship early in 1849. The story of Hudson's fall from grace has been told elsewhere in great detail[14] but, very briefly, for some years he had been paying shareholders higher dividends than were warranted by the profitability of his various lines by the simple expedient of paying them out of capital rather than revenue. The economic depression which first appeared in 1846 helped to ensure that traffic continued to fall short of expectations and inevitably questions began to be asked. A dubious transaction in York, Newcastle & Berwick Railway shares was queried at that company's half-yearly meeting in February 1849 which brought to light a number of similar transactions and doubtful practices elsewhere. Hudson was therefore obliged to resign from that board as well as from the boards of the Midland and York & North Midland Railways. Committees of Inquiry were set up by the shareholders of all four companies and the damning reports from these committees led to Hudson's eventual complete downfall.

The York & North Midland Railway Committee of Inquiry

The committee set up to investigate the affairs of the Y&NMR first sat in York on 31 May 1849 and remained in session for fourteen weeks,[15] after which four reports were issued dealing with every aspect of the railway's business. Thomas Cabry appeared before the committee on several occasions and was examined at length, his first appearance being 27 to 29 June. He was questioned initially about his railway experience and he said he had been connected with railways all his life and had made 'with my own hands every part of a locomotive engine'. He was also questioned regarding engine orders placed with Kitson & Co. and in particular whether they should have been charged to capital or revenue account. It emerged that the company's book-keeping was somewhat chaotic, with very little prior agreement from the board to Cabry's expenditure which he undertook in accordance with what he saw as necessity. He never made any written returns to the board and assumed Hudson carried it all in his own head. It is interesting to note that, when repairing engines, Cabry always made 'a point of increasing the length and increasing the power of the engines'. However, if he was referring to lengthening the stroke, this would have involved new cylinders, a new crank axle and probably new motion. Such extensive alterations can hardly have been undertaken on many loco-

motives passing through the repair shops. He was quizzed at some length about the present value of the locomotive stock but, although he knew them well, he felt he could not make a 'quick exact estimate'. Apparently Robert Stephenson had gone through the whole stock and said that it was never in better condition. However Cabry said 'Robert Stephenson could merely give a matter of opinion'.

In another reference to the Kitson contract Cabry said he had no formal arrangement for consulting the directors and that it was 'always understood, I have no written order'. He admitted however that he didn't inform them directly – 'I made an arrangement for stock. I suppose the directors knew'. At the instigation of the manager, Peter Clarke, hydraulic cranes were being installed at Hull and it is obvious that Cabry neither approved of these nor of Clarke making it clear that it was not on his recommendation. When questioned about the possible benefit of the new cranes he said they were only used for loading and unloading goods and that there were apparently no specially trained men to operate them as 'every man who does a thing does it his own way. I have no doubt Mr Clarke thinks it best'.

With regard to permanent way matters a similar loose system of accounting came to light concerning repairs and renewals. Cabry himself kept no books, merely certifying accounts due for payment. As he only submitted paybills for work done, Cabry refused to be drawn on whether the annual cost of working and expenditure was a sufficient sum. 'You must understand, gentlemen, I have had a great deal to attend to. Not being my department alone. I do not mean to say that if I had not gone into it every week I might have given you an answer, I have not.'

Cabry's salary had been reduced from £1,000 to £800, presumably as part of the cut-back in expenditure in the company generally, and he was again pressed regarding his grip of annual expenditure. The questioner said he did not know how Cabry could consider himself the head of a department when he had no control of the details – 'They call you the head of this and they are making you the tail'. He was asked whether some track renewal costs had been paid for from the construction account which should properly have come from revenue, although the questioner conceded it was possible that if light rails were replaced with heavier ones the work might be properly charged to the construction account. Cabry reiterated that he had no written instructions on these matters but might well have discussed them with Hudson from time to time and felt that the whole matter was 'understood' rather than discussed. The committee was trying to obtain a breakdown of all expenditure but Cabry flatly informed them that he could not provide such details and that they were in just as good a position as he to find the information. Again he hinted that Clarke had brought a man from Brighton to take charge of the stores and that he had not been consulted on this subject.

Another interesting insight into contemporary operating practices arose in relation to buffers on goods wagons. Cabry did not think these were worth the expense and he coupled the wagons so that they were not more than four inches apart. He was asked whether coupling that close did not interfere with getting the train in motion. However he said this was not the case as the wagons could be coupled just far enough apart to ensure they would go round a curve without touching. No mention was made of the radius of the curve, however. It should be borne in mind that only springless 'dumb' buffers were fitted to goods vehicles at the time, their presence being far from indispensable.

The committee were obviously suspicious that Cabry had been receiving payments 'on the side' for placing orders with engine builders, and they asked him if it was usual to receive such a perquisite. He replied 'I can scarcely say, I never in my life received a single farthing, not a sixpence'. Nevertheless, at the Committee of Investigation into Hudson's machinations on the York, Newcastle & Berwick Railway which took place at about the same time, it emerged that he had paid Cabry £500 from YN&BR funds 'for having made some arrangement for procuring engines from Todd [Charles Todd the Leeds engine builder] for the company at a time when they were difficult to obtain'.[16] Apparently Cabry seems to have had some influence with Todd and used it to divert four engines ordered by the YN&MR to the YN&BR at Hudson's request. This payment came under fire at a YN&MR shareholders meeting on 29 November 1849 when it was described as 'for superintending the building of some engines'.[17]

This may have come in a somewhat different category to the 'perks' suggested by the YN&MR inquiry but it was nevertheless very generous bearing in mind the value of money at the time.

There had been several disputes with contractors over the new branches that were built in the late 1840s and Cabry felt that he could probably have undertaken the work himself with his own men without difficulty. At a later session Cabry was asked to give an opinion as to the probable expense of relaying the various lines in due course, but he pointed out that this would probably come all together and, although he knew the state of the lines well, he did not wish to state categorically how long they would last, suggesting that anybody who was asked would give a different opinion. He was pressed and said that Robert Stephenson might be a good choice to give such an opinion but the questioner interrupted and said 'I would sooner have yours than Robert Stephenson's' to which Cabry replied 'Well, it's one of those things we are a great deal in the dark about' – as we shall see later, the permanent way was to become his speciality after the formation of the North Eastern Railway in 1854. Cabry was asked whether he could make a year-by-year comparative valuation of rolling stock and whilst he said that this was probably possible he pointed out that 'some of our rolling stock is never seen for months'.

The company's architect G. T. Andrews was examined on 25 July regarding problems being encountered with the station at Church Fenton. It seems the directors could not decide whether to have the normal platform on each side of the line or one long platform with a cross-over in the middle so that passengers would not have to cross the line. Apparently John Cass Birkinshaw, the resident engineer for the construction of the various new YN&MR branches, thought the single platform was the best plan but Cabry was against it. It would seem that at the time of the inquiry the best arrangement had still not been decided as Andrews indicated that the roof had been ordered but was lying on site at the time – he thought Hudson did not like the look of it.

Cabry was examined again on 5 September and was questioned about the amount of stores in his workshop which the committee considered were rather low. He said 'it appears very low to me, but they were taken without my interference in the matter at all. Mr. Clarke has taken the management of that'. Another indication of his dislike of Clarke.

The principal contribution that Thomas Cabry made to the proceedings was undoubtedly in connection with the permanent way and he produced an estimate of future expenditure on renewals which extended over 36 years and spread, or 'equalised', the cost over this period. This plan was recommended by the committee to be implemented by the company and was chosen in preference to a similar estimate by Birkinshaw. They both produced detailed tables of the state of the Y&NMR track at the time of the report which are of interest as they show the superior quality of the original mileage of the railway laid at the time of the opening in 1839. The sleepers had been Kyanised and the rails were found to be 'as good as when laid down 13 years ago'. Apparently the only reason they required replacing was that, due to their light construction, they tended to spring when the heavier loads of the time passed over them. The iron rails available at the time of the report were not found to be of such good quality as the originals, probably due to the greater quantities that by then had to be produced. In addition the sleepers used on the later Y&NMR lines were of 'unprepared' timber and not treated with any preservative. In his report Cabry recommended another preserving process invented by John Bethell as it was thought to be as effective but cheaper. The Hull & Selby, in common with a number of other lines, had also been laid with Kyanised sleepers when it opened in 1840 and the older Leeds & Selby was still mostly laid with stone blocks which had been widely used, especially on railways built before the mid 1830s. The process of Kyanising consisted of placing the well-dried baulks of timber in open tanks filled with perchloride of mercury and leaving them in for a time equal to one day per inch of the widest side of the section. Penetration usually amounted to about a quarter of an inch. This method continued to be used on the Great Western Railway to preserve its many timber viaducts in the West Country until the last such structure was replaced in 1934.[18] In addition to its preservative qualities, Kyanising also

reduced the flammability of the timber. The tables produced for the report also showed that 18½ miles of the H&SR were laid using longitudinal sleepers, presumably similar to those of Brunel on the GWR,[19] the last of which were not replaced on the H&SR until 1860.[20]

Apparently 47 patents were taken out for timber preservation between 1737 and 1849, the processes of Kyan and Bethell being amongst those most frequently used.[21]

Cabry also produced a report on the rolling stock of the company jointly with James Fenton the Leeds engine builder. Cabry offered to enter into a contract with his employer, the Y&NMR, for either repairs and renewals or the entire working costs including provision of labour and materials, but his offer was not accepted. As will be seen later, he was quite keen on this idea and this was neither the first nor last time he would make such an offer.

The Leeds & Selby line had been virtually disused ever since it had been leased in 1840 and the committee's report brought this to light. Accordingly the board instructed Cabry to repair it to carry goods traffic and this work was completed by August 1849.[22]

All in all Cabry seems to have come through the inquiry quite well, given the obvious laxness of control which was rife in the company under Hudson. However he was evidently competent and conscientious and managed to survive the experience at a time when many heads rolled, including a number of directors. He may well have been the perfect foil for Hudson, quietly obeying instructions and not asking too many awkward questions; no doubt 'Veritas Vincit' would have seen him in this light. The Y&NMR minutes and other records become extremely detailed from this period on and there was a general tightening up in all departments of the railway, with a number of economies being instituted. All this was in stark contrast to the previous ten years under the rule of the 'Railway King'. Hudson and Cabry evidently had a genuine respect for one another and this is reflected in Hudson's almost invariable habit of sending Cabry in to 'trouble-shoot' any problems in the concerns which came under the Hudson umbrella.

CHAPTER FIVE

The Last Years of
the York & North Midland Railway

THE FALL of George Hudson was a watershed in Thomas Cabry's career. The heady and adventurous period of railway development of the previous twenty years was coming to an end and a much leaner time lay ahead. During the next two decades, covering the remainder of Cabry's working life, a much more sober atmosphere prevailed, partly because the railways were 'growing up' and partly because the early hopes of profitability, especially on rural branch lines, were not being realised. Against this background Thomas Cabry gained the respectability of middle age and had already entered local politics. There was no longer a 'Veritas Vincit' to point out any weaknesses in railway management that might have continued to exist.

One of the lines conceived by Hudson in 1847 was still being built after his departure from the scene. He had seen the benefit to be derived from the construction of a short connecting line between Burton Salmon, on the main line from York, to Altofts Junction (where the Y&NMR connected with the Midland Railway) and Knottingley, where a connection would be made with the Lancashire & Yorkshire Railway and thence via their line to Askern Junction where a further connection would be made with the Great Northern Railway, then being built. By the simple expedient of building a line 3¼ miles long Hudson would not only prevent the GNR from constructing their own line into York but would also give the Y&NMR an alternative route to London, at the same time bringing all traffic between King's Cross and the North East over Y&NMR metals. The planned route of the Knottingley Curve, as it became known, took it

across the Aire & Calder Navigation at Brotherton and, although it was originally intended that the bridge would be of three arches, early difficulties with the canal authorities led Robert Stephenson to design a tubular bridge with two tubes to cross the navigation in a single span.

The story of the bridge has been told more comprehensively elsewhere[1] but suffice it to say that it was less well known than Robert Stephenson's famous Conway and Britannia bridges in North Wales and, at 232 feet long, was only about half their length. As the Brotherton Tubular Bridge was built after Robert Stephenson had gained experience in this type of structure with the two Welsh bridges it is surprising that the width of the tubes at Brotherton was underestimated, being only ten feet approximately at the mid point between the deck and roof. This compares with 12½ feet at Menai and 14 feet at Conway. The Brotherton tubes tapered from bottom to top unlike the other bridges which were of rectangular box section with stiffening plates in cellular form at top and bottom. Even with the narrow rolling stock of the period clearances were very tight and shortly after the first tube was opened there were a number of minor incidents. The GNR complained to the Y&NMR who took the matter to Robert Stephenson. He defended his choice of width and quoted several equally narrow tunnels in use elsewhere in the country. However he omitted to mention that several of these 'equally narrow' tunnels were on other lines he had engineered and were proving equally troublesome. Nevertheless, as the Knottingley branch was ostensibly built only to provide access to its immediate locality, it is just possible

The Tubular Bridge at Brotherton

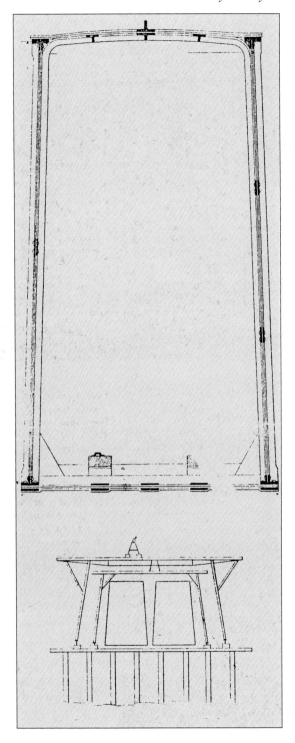

11. Plans showing the original tubes of Brotherton Bridge together with the wooden scaffolding used in their construction. *Zeitschrift für Bauwesen 1853 Jahrg. III no. V. VI Bl.44 – Rohrenbrücke über die Aire bei Brotherton*

12. The Knottingley Curve

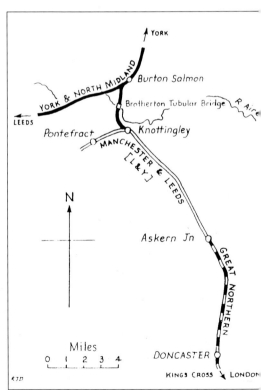

13. *(above)* The Tubular Bridge at Brotherton. *National Railway Museum*

14. *(left)* A view of Brotherton Bridge from the line, clearly showing the extra plates added at the top to widen the tubes. *National Railway Museum*

15. Brotherton Bridge as it is today. A number of stone courses have been removed to lower the capstones of the abutments to the level of the retaining walls of the bridge approaches. The stone plaques of 1850 were renewed in 1903 and now commemorate the building of the bridge and the replacement of the superstructure in that year. *Author*

that the bridge was not built to proportions approaching Stephenson's other tubular bridges lest it should appear an unduly imposing structure on a minor branch line and therefore reveal Hudson's true motives.

A lengthy harangue ensued between the two railway companies, the government inspectorate and Stephenson, who felt that the main problem lay in the wider than average carriages that the GNR used at that time. The GNR was quite rightly concerned about the effects that such a narrow bridge would have on future carriage design as the Brotherton tubes only gave a clearance of 16½ inches on each side which was considered inadequate on a trunk route. More modern rolling stock would have fitted extremely snugly if the bridge had been left in its original condition.

To resolve the problem Robert Stephenson at first suggested the removal of the angle irons at the junctions of the bridge sections to increase the interior width by six inches, but the Government Inspector was not prepared to accept this small increase and eventually the more expensive expedient of inserting 21½ inch plates to widen the roof of the tube was resorted to, making the sides vertical. This, together with removal of the angle irons, gave a clear internal width of just over 11 feet 6 inches – an increase of one and a half feet.

Whilst the branch line and the bridge were being constructed Birkinshaw was in charge of the works under Robert Stephenson, but when the plan to widen the tubes was implemented Cabry appeared to become more involved. He was able to report to the board that he had opened the second tube for traffic on 11 October 1852.[2] This was the first one to be altered as its use had been prevented by the Government Inspector who claimed not to have noticed the inadequate width of the first tube when approving its opening for traffic. The original tube was then altered and opened for traffic on 16 November[3] and the bridge was finally completed in the summer of 1853, Cabry having been told to complete the abutments on 15 June.[4] So ended a long-running battle with the Board of Trade which had been rumbling on since the Knottingley curve was first opened to traffic in early 1850. The tubes were replaced in 1903 by a more conventional steel bridge which is still in use today.

During this period Cabry drove the engine for a number of Royal trains. The earliest record was on the occasion of the visit of Queen Victoria and Prince Albert to Newcastle to open the Central Station and the Royal Border Bridge at Berwick on 29 August 1850 on their way to Scotland. Having left London (Euston) on 27 August they stayed at the great Yorkshire house of Castle Howard as the guests of the Earl of Carlisle. On the morning of 29 August they travelled over the Y&NMR from Castle Howard to York, where the York, Newcastle & Berwick Railway took over. The *Yorkshire Gazette* reported that 'Mr. Cabry, the engineer, personally directed the engine which was elegantly decorated…'[5] The Royal party returned from Balmoral a few weeks later, travelling from Edinburgh to London on 11 October,[6] and south of York they were hauled by a Y&NMR engine once again driven by Thomas Cabry.[7] Cabry brought Royalty into York on their way north to Edinburgh in September 1852[8] and drove the engine which followed the Royal train on a similar journey two years later.[9] He was also noted in the *Yorkshire Gazette* on various other occasions between 1855 and 1858 as being in the official parties meeting Royal trains at York.[10]

Following a report by Cabry and others in February 1851 on the state of the line, improvements in signalling were authorised, together with provision of new sidings at various locations, and the continuing poor state of the track of the Leeds & Selby section was also considered. It was decided to reduce the passenger trains to two per day and impose speed restrictions on that line where necessary until relaying was completed.[11] Part of the materials required to improve the L&S section came from the second line of rails on the recently built Selby to Market Weighton branch where traffic had not by then justified a double line.[12]

The protection of wooden sleepers continued to receive attention. Although the Kyanising process had been used during the construction of the original route of the Y&NMR, by the late 1840s Cabry favoured the Bethell process. In his report to the

Y&NMR Committee of Inquiry in 1849 he had indicated this preference and had subsequently introduced it on the Y&NMR. The Bethell process utilised creosote as the preserving agent and there were two ways of impregnating the timbers, under pressure or by open-tank immersion. Cabry had originally been in favour of the former but, when in April 1850 he went to observe methods on the London & North Western Railway,[13] Robert Benson Dockray, one of that company's officers, persuaded him that the open-tank method was better. It is of interest that Dockray mentions Cabry in his diaries.[14] Apparently the two engineers spent much of their time discussing George Hudson and Cabry 'spoke very kindly of him' praising his unstinting support of his staff in times of difficulty. Cabry felt sure that it was only after Hudson overreached himself when purchasing his country estate at Newby Park in Yorkshire that he was forced to 'raise money by all sorts of objectionable means with the full intention of repaying them'.

Cabry also visited the Bethell works at Greenwich and sought the opinion of Robert Stephenson and George Parker Bidder, another prominent engineer of the time, before reporting in favour of the process to his board.[15] The board approved his plans for tanks and drying houses on 24 May, and these were built at Milford and continued in use until 1874 when the North Eastern Railway built a new plant at Hartlepool, closing both Milford and a similar depot at Middlesbrough.[16] J. Bethell & Co. of Grimsby expressed an interest in the old Milford works but it is not recorded whether they purchased the site.[17]

It is interesting to note that in 1850, on Cabry's recommendation, 140 tons of cast-iron sleepers of W. H. Barlow's patent had been supplied by John Walker of York who had also supplied ironwork for the rebuilding of the Ulleskelf bridge in 1843.[18] These sleepers were apparently only used to support rail joints.[19]

A number of canals in Y&NMR territory had been purchased by Hudson in 1847. One of these was the Market Weighton Canal and in 1851 its general condition necessitated some urgent work being undertaken, this being yet another aspect of railway management which fell within Cabry's responsibility. He was authorised to make a number of repairs to the locks[20] and continued to be respon-

16. The Royal Train at Castle Howard Station on 29 August 1850. The occasion is the visit of Queen Victoria and Prince Albert to the Earl of Carlisle, prior to opening Newcastle Central Station and the Royal Border Bridge at Berwick, and on their way to Scotland by train. The locomotive was driven by Thomas Cabry. *'Illustrated London News', 31.8.1850*

sible for canal maintenance well into the NER era.

Sub-contracting work rather than employing direct labour, so much in vogue today, was practised by many early railways. The working of trains was one such task, and track maintenance was another. The Y&NMR board considered the latter in 1842;[21] Cabry obtained tenders, and, whilst one was accepted, nothing more was done. In 1849 the idea was revived, apparently again without result. Cabry, with other engineers, advised a sub-committee of the Great Northern Railway board in 1851 concerning the working of their line under contract and also the siting of their repair shops. E. B. Wilson, the locomotive builder of Leeds,[22] tried unsuccessfully for a contract to repair the GNR rolling stock.[23]

The Y&NMR had purchased a number of locomotives and other rolling stock from Wilson,[24] and Thomas Cabry and his wife were evidently friends of the family as they were staying with the Wilsons at Arthington Hall near Leeds on the night of the Census on 30 March 1851.[25]

Late in 1851 Thomas Cabry was called to appear before an arbitration hearing in the case of Gray v. The London & North Western Railway Company.[26] It will be remembered that John Gray had taken out a patent for his variable expansion valve gear[27] whilst he was in the employ of the Liverpool & Manchester Railway before his appointment on the Hull & Selby Railway. Gray later became the proprietor of an iron foundry in Chester but was declared bankrupt in 1850.[28] He had for several years been pursuing claims against the L&NWR for infringement of his valve gear patent and the case came up before the South Lancashire Assizes in August 1851.[29] In view of the technical nature of the claim it was referred to arbitration, the hearing being in London in October and November 1851.

A number of expert witnesses were called by the L&NWR including Daniel Gooch of the GWR, James Fenton of Leeds, Brunel, Joseph Locke, William Fairbairn and Thomas Cabry. Quite an impressive array but the L&NWR did stand to lose £5,000, the provisional amount of damages awarded by the assize court, subject to arbitration.[30] Not surprisingly Gray was only able to muster a more modest group of witnesses but did produce William Dodds[31] and Bennet Woodcroft[32] together with several other engineers and engine drivers.

Cabry was called on 6 November 1851, the eighth day of the hearing. As has been mentioned in an earlier chapter, two locomotives, the *Ariel* and the *Antelope,* had been purchased by the Y&NMR in September 1840. These were fitted with Gray's valve gear which either Gray or Charles Todd (or both – Cabry could not quite recall) had

induced Cabry to try on the Y&NMR. Gray's gear had been removed and replaced by Stephenson's link motion in 1843 (the first application of it on that line) due to difficulties in reversing the gear. Cabry stated that 13 engines fitted with Gray's gear had been acquired with the Hull & Selby in 1845. Again his memory was a little uncertain and, according to various researchers,[33] 15 H&SR engines had been fitted although one was scrapped before 1845. However three had subsequently been fitted with the link motion by the Y&NMR. Of the remaining nine or so Cabry said most of these had remained idle since acquisition by the Y&NMR but three or four were worked occasionally.

Cabry had removed the gear from one of the idle engines and taken it to London, mounting it on wooden stilts to exhibit at the arbitration hearing. This resulted in the following amusing exchange which took place between Webster (Gray's counsel) and Cabry:

Where did that particular expansive gearing come from that is at the end of the room?

I brought it from York it was taken from one of the Engines that originally belonged to the Hull and Selby Railway.

Did you bring it with you in the train?

Yes.

Not in a first class carriage I hope.

No not in a carriage.

What engine did it come from?

I do not know the precise engine.

Did you ask the Directors leave?

No.

You brought it of your own motion as they say in law?
I do not know what you mean by that.
Was it your own idea to bring it?
Decidedly.
Who suggested it to you?
No one.

Webster tried to draw Cabry on the matter of his own valve gear. Cabry had to explain that the gear was his brother Henry's (this was neither the first nor the last time that this confusion arose) and that it had been abandoned after a few years and been superseded by the link motion. Cabry's vagueness over details of even quite recent events mildly irritated Webster and the reference to the valve gear being Henry's caused him to remark with thinly veiled sarcasm 'I am glad to hear there are two such gentlemen'. There was some discussion as to what constituted expansive working of steam and Cabry was adamant that provided the slide valve had lap then even the common gab motion was an expansive gear. Cabry was also quizzed about alterations made to various Y&NMR engines for reasons that are not completely clear. Gray may have had good cause to dislike Cabry. His valve gear had received short shrift at Cabry's hand and Gray made sure he was not around when Cabry took over the H&SR locomotive department with the alleged drop of standards referred to by 'Veritas Vincit' earlier. However there is nothing in Cabry's evidence to suggest any animosity between them and Cabry merely felt that Gray's gear had been replaced by a better alternative – as indeed had that of his brother Henry.

Gray ultimately lost his case but, as the transcript of the summing up is missing, it is impossible to know exactly what conclusions were drawn. The case was based on a long-standing claim, the details of which are outside the scope of this account. He died in straitened circumstances in October 1854.

A small independent line of about 17½ miles in length, the Hull & Holderness Railway was projected in 1852 and Cabry was appointed as engineer to the company.[34] Locking, the Y&NMR secretary, and Sherriff the goods manager were also to act in those capacities on the H&HR, with the agreement of the Y&NMR board,[35] although there was some adverse comment from Y&NMR shareholders at the half-yearly company meeting on 17 February 1854. However, the chairman assured them that the calls on their time would not be great and as the H&HR was to connect with their line it was to their advantage to have their officers in charge, especially as the Manchester, Sheffield & Lincolnshire Railway 'on the opposite side of the water' had put up strong opposition and would probably have stepped in if the Y&NMR had not.

The H&HR directors apparently had no intention of working the line themselves and nearly a year before the line was opened Cabry, who had shown interest in the principle of leasing before, wrote to the board offering to lease the line for 21 years on his own account.[36] They were not prepared to decide about this at the time as they were also negotiating with the Y&NMR to work the traffic.[37] Agreement was reached on 16 September on this aspect but the Y&NMR were not willing to lease the line[38] and discussions with Cabry continued over the next six months[39] until, after several changes in the terms offered, Cabry rejected the company's final offer in a letter dated 17 April 1854.[40] The line opened to traffic on 24 June, worked by the Y&NMR which was shortly to become part of the NER.

Regarding Cabry's earlier negotiations over operation and maintenance of the H&HR, it is ironic to find that in 1863 the NER took over the working from the existing contractor, John Coulthard, at the expiration of his contract[41] and Cabry reported that he hoped to save £200 a year by so doing.[42]

A branch line to the Victoria Dock at Hull was projected in October 1851 when Cabry and Sherriff met a deputation from the Hull Dock Company.[43] Cabry was the engineer in charge of construction and was paid £250 for his services.[44] A joint venture between the Y&NMR and the Hull Dock Co., the branch was opened to goods traffic on 16 May 1853 and for passengers two weeks later on 1 June.[45] The H&HR had originally intended to build its own terminus in Hull but approached the Y&NMR with a view to sharing the projected terminus at the end of the latter's Victoria Dock branch to save costs. This terminus, to Cabry's design, was built at the joint expense of the Y&NMR and the H&HR,[46] who used it from 27 June 1854 when the H&HR opened for traffic. The only engineering work of any note on the branch was a swing bridge over the river Hull and Cabry was responsible for its erection, with ironwork provided by Beecroft Butler & Co. of Kirkstall, Leeds.[47]

CHAPTER SIX

The North Eastern Era

THE FORMATION of the North Eastern Railway by the amalgamation of the York & North Midland, the York, Newcastle & Berwick and the Leeds Northern Railways took place on 31 July 1854. Various operating and financial advantages had brought this about and it was to have a profound effect on Thomas Cabry's future career. Thomas Elliot Harrison, who was not only engineer but also general manager of the YN&BR, had master-minded the amalgamation of the three companies and continued as general manager of the NER until 26 October 1854, when he resigned in favour of Captain William O'Brien, the secretary, and himself became engineer-in-chief. Edward Fletcher, locomotive superintendent since 1845 of the Newcastle & Darlington Junction Railway (which became part of the York & Newcastle Railway, later the YN&BR, in 1846) was appointed to the same position for the whole of the newly-formed NER. His association with Harrison probably made him a natural choice for this post. Fletcher was a younger man than Cabry and had worked under him on the Canterbury & Whitstable Railway and later during the construction of the Y&NMR. In fact a joint locomotive committee had been formed on 1 April 1853 and Fletcher had control of all the locomotives of the three constituent companies from that date.[1] After the official amalgamation a year later Cabry became the engineer of the Southern Division of the NER 'South of and including the Skerne Bridge' (near Darlington)[2] with responsibility for all civil engineering and permanent way matters. His territory covered all of the old Y&NMR together with the Leeds Northern and part of the YN&BR main line. A full-time architect, Thomas Prosser, was appointed, no doubt further narrowing Cabry's field of responsibility.

At the time of the amalgamation Cabry, who received £700 a year and a free house,[3] was the highest paid officer of the NER after Harrison, who was paid £1,200 a year for 'not less than half his time to be devoted to the service of the Company'. John Bourne, the engineer of the Northern Division (appointed on 1 January 1855), received £600 and a free house whilst Fletcher was in receipt of an annual salary of £600.[4] Cabry was to lose this financial advantage in later years, Fletcher finally overtaking him from 1 July 1863.[5] Had Hudson remained in charge of the Y&NMR the whole course of events would no doubt have been very different and Cabry might well have risen to higher things. In the event T. E. Harrison emerged as the principal figure and dominated NER affairs.

On 19 September 1854 part of the roof of Bramhope Tunnel, north of Leeds, collapsed and a train from Stockton to Leeds ran into the obstruction. The shock of the impact caused the rear part of the train to break away and run back down the incline. Although this portion was brought safely to a halt at Arthington station, a further open carriage which had also broken away almost immediately ran into it causing a number of serious injuries.[6] On the following day Cabry was on the scene, having been taken to the north end of the tunnel by a light engine. He gave directions to the driver to wait outside until his return and entered the tunnel. Whilst he was inspecting the damage two ex-LNR men,

Gazlett the Leeds District Passenger Super-intendent and another employee named Pepper, commandeered the engine and took it back to Starbeck. A goods train was already standing on their line at Starbeck and, as a collision was inevitable, the driver and fireman leapt off the engine. Pepper followed them and broke his leg whilst Gazlett stayed on the engine and fractured several ribs. The driver of the requisitioned engine had passed a signal at danger and was prosecuted. How long Cabry had to wait at Bramhope before he got a lift home is not related but the former LNR men paid dearly for what appears to have been a bit of inter-company rivalry.[7]

The acquisition of the Whitby & Pickering Railway by the Y&NMR has already been mentioned and by 1857 the original 40 h.p. stationary engine on the Goathland Incline was proving inadequate as traffic demands grew and trains became heavier. Fletcher submitted a plan to the board for enlarge-ment of the engine and this work was undertaken by J. Burlinson & Co. who completed the work in September 1858 at a cost of £650.[8]

At about the same time Thomas Cabry designed a larger special brake van similar to the one designed by his brother Henry, the NER company minutes stating 'That a break be constructed upon the plan adopted on the Railways in Belgium to be used on the Goathland Incline'.[9] This brake van had six wheels and two sets of sledge brakes and had a strong iron frame and weighed 11 tons 6 cwt.[10] Besides being an expense and inconvenience to the company the incline was a source of danger and there were three accidents between 1860 and 1864 – two minor and one more serious.

The first of these, on 29 August 1860, involved the 6.35pm train from York to Whitby. The train consisting of seven carriages and a guard's van arrived at the top of the incline at 9.05pm. As usual the engine ran round its train and gently shunted it towards the waiting special brake van, to which was attached the rope from the stationary engine. All went well during the descent and the brakesman only found it necessary to apply one set of sledge brakes in addition to the normal brake which was applied at the rear by the train guard. The special brake van was then released from the rope near the bottom of the incline, running forward into a siding whilst the train continued towards the engine

which was waiting to take the train on to Whitby. Unfortunately several fish trains had passed up the incline during the day, leaving the rails in a slippery state. The train hit the waiting engine at about 4 mph and, although little damage was done, three passengers were slightly injured. The Board of Trade Inspector's report was critical of the working arrangements and recommended that the incline van should not be detached until the train had come to rest at the foot of the incline (which, he said, the company had since put into practice).[11]

The second accident occurred on 12 October 1861 when four wagons, laden with stone and with the incline brake van at the rear, were ascending the incline. The rope snapped and the brakesman, unable to hold the train, jumped off to sprag the wheels, which he also failed to do. The vehicles ran back down the incline and collided with four more stone wagons which were waiting to ascend and had been left, against the regulations, on the main line instead of in a siding. The same railway inspector, Captain Tyler, was sent to investigate and he noted that the special incline van was 'broken to pieces'.[12] This was probably one of the original smaller vans still being used in addition to Cabry's larger van built in 1858. The Act authorising a deviation to replace the Goathland Incline with a line capable of locomotive haulage, was given the Royal Assent on 11 July 1861. It was therefore particularly unfortun-ate that a yet another accident occurred only five months before the opening of the new line.

This final accident on the old incline involved the 6.45pm train from York on 10 February 1864 in snowy weather. The rope broke soon after the train had started down, with the incline van leading as usual. The brakesman applied both pairs of sledge brakes but these were ineffective due to snow and ice on the line. He then attempted to put sand on the rails, not realising that the pipes of the sanding gear were also frozen. As he could do nothing more he then jumped for his life. The van, together with its train of four carriages and the normal brake van in the rear, gathered speed and as the sledge brakes were fully applied the weight of the brake van was borne by the sledges and not the wheels. The wheel flanges were therefore unable to guide the van which left the rails on a right hand curve 300 yards beyond the foot of the incline. Although the sledges were flanged to the same profile as the wheels, and might have kept the van on the rails, their mountings were not strong enough to resist the lateral pressure of the curve and collapsed under the strain. Unfortunately there was a substantial stack of timber beside the line in the path of the derailed van which shattered its superstructure upon impact and severely damaged three of the four carriages. Two passengers were crushed to death in the leading carriage and thirteen others were injured.

According to the evidence of the Whitby locomotive superintendent E. Laws the iron sledges were frequently renewed; nevertheless those on the van at the time of the accident were 'indented with grooves not parallel to the flanges'.[13] The inspecting officer, once again Captain Tyler, was highly critical of the company's arrangements which allowed two ropes to break in such a short time and the condition of the rope was of course part of Cabry's responsibility as engineer. Cabry said that he inspected the rope from time to time but left the stationary engineman to turn the rope when he thought fit and report any defects. At the inquest into the two deaths the coroner's jury considered the rope to be so worn as to be unfit for use.[14] Despite the short life remaining for the incline equipment before the new line was due to open, the NER was obliged to renew the rope once again and to rebuild the shattered incline van. Cabry reported that the new rope was fitted on 27 February and the van was back in use by 3 March. Immediately after the accident maximum permitted loads were reduced and two old brake vans were brought back into use. Cabry suggested to Fletcher that the newer brake van should be fitted with a spring draw bar (presumably to cushion any sudden jerks on the rope) but it is not clear whether this idea was implemented.[15] Somewhat belatedly the board decided to provide telegraphic communication between the top and bottom of the incline. This replaced the somewhat haphazard arrangement whereby the train at the bottom was attached to the rope and then set back a little to jerk the rope as a signal to the engineman at the top of the incline to commence winding. Although the accidents on the Whitby & Pickering section accentuated the unsatisfactory nature of the sledge brake, slack operating methods on the Goathland Incline were without doubt a contributory factor.

17. The house at no.31 The Mount where Thomas and Margaret Cabry spent their last years. It is now the Carlton House Hotel. *Author*

Another small line with which Thomas Cabry senior was associated was the Nidd Valley Branch from Harrogate to Pateley Bridge, of which the first sod was turned in September 1860.[16] This was constructed by the NER and whilst Harrison was the consulting engineer, Cabry was in charge of the building works. The line opened on 1 May 1862.

After three years in office, Cabry had resigned as Councillor for the Micklegate Ward in 1850 but re-entered civic life as Sheriff of York, to which office he was unanimously elected on 9 November 1860. Two years later on 12 December 1862 he was elected an alderman and on 9 November 1864 the office of Lord Mayor was conferred on him. It was not in fact his turn for election but Alderman Wade, whose turn it should have been, had suffered a recent bereavement and it was felt he should not be nominated. In putting Cabry's name forward his suitability for the post was emphasised and Mrs Cabry was described as 'a lady of greatest possible ability and grace of manners'.[17] However he did not feel his railway duties would allow him to take up the office and he therefore paid the customary £100 fine. In the meantime Wade decided he could in fact stand and was duly elected.[18] Nevertheless to express his appreciation of the honour conferred on him Cabry presented a stained-glass window to the Guildhall representing the confirmation of Magna Carta by Edward I in a Parliament held in York in January 1298.[19] Unfortunately this window was destroyed by a bomb during the Second World War.[20]

Thomas and his wife had lived in Holgate Villa since 1844 but in the summer of 1865 they moved to 31 The Mount, a property built in about 1825 and in which Cabry had acquired an interest on 10 June 1850 when 'an undivided moiety' had been conveyed to him from his wife's brother George Bookless.[21] The house had been let since 1851.

The North Eastern Railway's bridge replacement programme

PERHAPS the major undertaking in the 1850s and '60s with which Cabry's name was associated was the programme of replacement of some 80 timber bridges and viaducts on the Southern Division of the NER. Whilst many of these were small structures, a good number were more substantial and Thomas Cabry was in charge of the whole rebuilding operation, which was carried out over a period of 15 years.

Timber had proved a cheap and attractive material and had saved on initial building costs, particularly on lines passing through difficult country. In common with similar structures on, for instance, the Scottish Central Railway and the Norfolk Railway, it was no doubt planned from the outset that replacement by more durable material would be carried out from revenue once the lines were generating income, but the period of financial stringency on the Y&NMR after Hudson's fall from grace may have delayed the commencement of the work. The fairly early replacement of bridges and viaducts in Yorkshire is in stark contrast to Brunel's viaducts in Devon and Cornwall, some of which lasted well into the twentieth century. Several Y&NMR viaducts were converted into embankments which did not happen in the west of England where the valleys being crossed were on the whole much deeper.

Timber may actually have been preferred where a long low viaduct was used instead of an embankment as it was probably quicker as well as cheaper to construct. Another factor to be considered is the lack of a long clear span, as all timber bridges had supports at frequent intervals. A good example of this limitation was the Bubwith Viaduct, on the Selby to Market Weighton line, where cast-iron girders were used over the river to give adequate clearance in one span, the approach spans being of timber. However, Brunel did design a span of more than 250 feet in timber for the projected bridge over the river Tamar at Saltash but this was eventually built of wrought iron due to stringent Admiralty stipulations regarding headroom and minimum span.[22] Danger from fire and the problem of adequate protection of the wood from rot were other factors to be considered but higher maintenance costs in the days of abundant cheap labour and suitable timber would still have been preferable to high capital outlay especially if only for a limited time before planned rebuilding in brick, stone or iron. Brunel seems to have taken a different view as he designed his bridges to allow replacement of individual members without interrupting the traffic and indeed his last Cornish viaduct, at Collegewood on the Falmouth branch, lasted until 1934.[23] Although routine replacement of defective parts must have taken place on the NER structures, no evidence has been found that the design took this into account in the same way as with Brunel's viaducts.

There were no timber structures on the original route of the Y&NMR but the company made extensive use of them on the subsequent lines built in the late 1840s and early 1850s, as did several other companies which became part of the NER in 1854.

Precise details of Cabry's methods of reconstruction have not survived but it would seem likely that, whenever possible, he adopted similar techniques to those employed when rebuilding the Wharfe Bridge at Ulleskelf, described in an earlier chapter. On double lines this would have involved temporary singling of the track at the site of the bridge being rebuilt and would not have interrupted the traffic over the line.

All timber bridges and viaducts on the Southern Division of the NER were replaced by the end of 1869.

The timber viaducts and bridges on the Southern Division of the North Eastern Railway and their replacements under Thomas Cabry's supervision. 1855–1869

18. The Hutton Viaduct as it is today. The girders have been replaced but the piers, supporting cast-iron grillage and piles date from 1866/7 when the original timber structure was replaced. They should be compared with those of bridge no.45 on the Grosmont–Whitby section with which they are virtually identical. *Author*

York–Scarborough line
(Opened 8 July 1845)

Hutton Viaduct

400 feet total length. From the western end there were four approach spans of 20 feet span, four of 50 feet span and one of 25 feet span – all on a skew of 28 degrees.[24] OS map ref. 764678

A substantial viaduct over the river Derwent. Rebuilt 1866/7[25] as a wrought-iron girder bridge supported on two oblique brick piers founded on cast-iron grillings and piles.

Cherry Farm Viaduct No.1

One span of 25 feet and five of 12 feet. OS map ref. 774698

Cherry Farm Viaduct No.2

One span of 25 feet and six of 12 feet. OS map ref. 776701

Both these viaducts were later filled in and the river Derwent diverted.

19. A timber bridge leading to Malton station, Y&NMR. Although this bridge was only used for road traffic and to carry a siding it was of similar design to the other timber bridges on the Y&NMR.
National Railway Museum

20. The bridge at Malton after rebuilding in 1869.
From a postcard in the J. Stone Collection

Malton Bridge

OS map ref. 787715

Rebuilt as a wrought-iron girder bridge *c.*1869 with two spans of 48 feet supported by a row of six cast-iron columns in mid river at a skew of 20 degrees. This bridge originally carried a siding to a mill as well as the road from Malton town centre to the station. It now carries only the road and remains virtually as rebuilt, the rails having since been covered with tarmac.[26]

Norton Viaduct

A low viaduct of 62 spans of 12 feet over the edge of the river Derwent. OS map ref. 792714

Rebuilt 1866/7[27] but replaced by an embankment in 1882, reducing the width of the river.[28]

Muston & Jerdingham Drain Viaduct

15 spans of 25 feet. OS map ref. 007802

Rebuilt 1863.[29]

Some small bridges and culverts were replaced in 1856[30] and the remainder between 1863 and 1869.[31]

Rillington–Pickering line

(Opened 8 July 1845)

Marishes Bridge

A long low viaduct with one span of 20 feet and 64 spans of 12 feet. OS map ref. 834775

The approaches to the river Derwent crossing were filled in between 1858 and 1859.[32] The bridge itself was replaced between 1863 and 1869.[33] The girders were removed shortly after the line was closed in 1966 and the abutments have since also been removed.

Pickering Beck

Five spans of 12 feet. OS map ref. 797839

Rebuilt between 1863 and 1869.[34] The line was closed in 1966 and the track lifted but the bridge, with wrought-iron girders supported on two rows of six cast-iron columns, is still in place.

Six small bridges were replaced between 1863 and 1869.[35]

Selby–Market Weighton line

(Opened 1 August 1848)

Bubwith Viaduct

A long low viaduct of timber with a central 70 foot span of cast-iron girders over the river Derwent. There were 52 timber spans of 20 feet, mostly on the west bank of the river. Total length 400 yards. OS map ref. 707355

The timber approaches on the west side of the river were burnt down on the night of 2 August 1858 and the approaches on both sides of the river were rebuilt in brick.* The central span remained of cast-iron girder construction. The line was closed in 1965 and the track removed but the brick approaches remain.

* Although it was believed that a cinder falling from the engine of the 8pm train from Selby started the fire, it was not discovered until 6am the next day.[36] Thomas Cabry was reported as having been 'early on the spot and directed operations'. The rebuilt bridge was re-opened on 18 April 1859.[37]

Burton Salmon–Knottingley line

(Opened 3 March 1850)

Knottingley Viaduct

Total length 570 yards. OS map ref. 245482

This viaduct was gradually filled in to become an embankment between 1857 and 1861.[38]

Thirsk–Malton line

(Opened 1 June 1853)

Malton Viaduct

Seven approach spans on the north side of the river Derwent, two spans across the river and four approach spans on the south side. OS map ref. 794715

The rebuilding of this double-line bridge was completed in December 1866, the work having taken nearly a year.[39]

It consisted of three spans of wrought-iron girders, the central span being of 72 feet and the approach spans of 44 and 41 feet respectively. On the north side, part of the timber viaduct was filled in as an

21. Malton Bridge from the river level showing the six cast-iron columns of 1869. These columns are identical to those at bridge no.55 at Ruswarp (FIG.35), rebuilt in the same year. *Author*

22. The same bridge taken from the west. It is of similar design to several on the Esk Valley line and the distinctive balustrade is similar to bridges 46, 47 and 48 on that line. Other such balustrades can be found on former NER lines. *Author*

embankment at this time. The line was closed in 1964 and the viaduct has since been dismantled, only some of the stone piers remaining.

Five small bridges rebuilt over several years from 1862.[40]

East & West Yorkshire Junction Railway
(Opened in stages between 1848 and 1851)

Marston Skip Bridge
One span of 32 feet and four of 28 feet (over the river Nidd). OS map ref. 557486

This timber bridge was repaired in 1863 and rebuilt in wrought iron in 1875.[41] The present structure is of recent origin.

Leeds & Thirsk Railway
(Opened in stages during 1848)

Ripon Viaduct No.1
Five spans of 33 feet. OS map ref. 318717
Rebuilt by early 1869.[42]

Ripon Viaduct No.2
(over the river Ure)
13 spans of 50 feet and one of 36 feet. OS map ref. 317720

Rebuilt with wrought-iron girders supported by six groups of three cast-iron columns. At each end of the viaduct a stone pier supported a further span to approach embankments.The rebuilding was completed by early 1869.[43] In the 1950s the bases of the columns were encased in concrete and alterations were also made to the tops of the columns. The line was closed in 1969 and the viaduct was dismantled in 1972.

Malton–Driffield line
(Opened 1 June 1853)

Wharram Viaduct
OS map ref. 856656
Filled up shortly after 1864.[44]

A number of other timber bridges were rebuilt shortly after 1864.[45]

Pickering–Grosmont line
(Opened 26 May 1836 by the Whitby & Pickering Railway for horse traffic and by the York & North Midland Railway for locomotives on 8 July 1845)

Fen Bogs Viaduct
A ¼ mile long structure at ground level over marshy land. It was built on timber piles which were sunk 25–50 feet to reach solid ground. OS map ref. 853978

Filled up using 30,000 cubic yards of earth in 1864.[46] The line is now operated by the North Yorkshire Moors Railway.

19 small bridges and two cattle arches were also replaced between 1863 and 1869.[47]

Grosmont–Whitby (Esk Valley) line
(Opened 8 June 1835 for horse traffic and 8 July 1845 for locomotives)

The history of the bridges in the Esk Valley is somewhat complicated and it has not been possible from surviving records to ascertain the exact sequence of events in all cases. When the Whitby & Pickering Railway opened as a horse-drawn line in 1835, all nine bridges over the river Esk were of light timber construction. When the Y&NMR purchased the line in 1845 it was rebuilt to take locomotives and four of these bridges were rebuilt with cast-iron girders resting on stone abutments and piers. Several bridges were washed away and replaced in the 1850s and the five remaining timber bridges were replaced between 1866 and 1869.[48] *The Illustrated London News* reported on 4 September 1869 that with the opening of the rebuilt Ruswarp Viaduct all the timber bridges in the Esk Valley and Vale of Goathland had been replaced. In the following list the bridges are given their British Rail numbers, and location where applicable, with further details taken from plans at BR York and from recent observation. Whilst some of the original timber bridges are shown on the plans at York, together with their replacements, the plans are unfortunately not dated. This stretch of line is of particular interest as so many bridges cross the river in a short distance and many of them are largely unchanged since the mid nineteenth century. Unless otherwise stated, the

23. Ripon Viaduct (NO.2) showing LNER A3 class 4-6-2 no.2508 *Brown Jack* crossing with a northbound express during the 1930s. This viaduct is another replacement of a timber structure and was completed in 1869. It was on a much larger scale than the Derwent or Esk Valley structures and was demolished in 1972, following closure of the Thirsk–Harrogate line. *J. W. Hague, by courtesy of David V. Beeken*

wrought-iron work of the bridges listed below is of similar age and appearance to the bridge over the Derwent at Malton, connecting the town with the station, mentioned above. This is known to date from *c.*1869 and makes it fairly certain that the Esk Valley bridges still contain much of Cabry's work.

Bridge No.44

Four spans of 42 feet each.
OS map ref. 829057

The first replacement was with cast-iron girders, supported by three stone piers and abutments, in 1845.[49] The girders were replaced in 1884.

Bridge No.45

Two spans of 50 feet each.
OS map ref. 834060

The timber bridge here lasted until the 1860s [50] when it was replaced by wrought-iron girders on a central pier of stone supported by cast-iron grillage

24. Bridge no.45 of 1866/7. The similarity to the Hutton Viaduct (FIG 18) should be noted. *Author*

on cast-iron piles. The design of this pier is virtually identical to those of the Hutton Viaduct (mentioned above) so may well have been completed in 1866/7.

25. Bridge no.46. One of four bridges on the Esk Valley line, probably designed by G. T. Andrews in collaboration with Thomas Cabry, which replaced the original light timber structure when the Whitby & Pickering line was upgraded to take locomotives in 1845. The other five timber bridges on the line were probably replaced with heavier timber structures in 1845 which were gradually further replaced by the present bridges during the 1850s and 60s. Bridge no.44, longer and higher than the other three, is difficult to photograph due to the profusion of trees in the vicinity. *Author*

Bridge No.46

Two spans of 40 feet each.
OS map ref. 839061

The cast-iron girder bridge with central stone pier of 1845 was replaced in 1888 by wrought-iron girders.

Bridge No.47

Originally two spans of 50 feet each. Now one span of 93 feet 4 inches.
OS map ref. 845066

The cast-iron girder bridge with central stone pier of 1845 was replaced in 1888 with wrought-iron girders. However the central pier was badly damaged by floods in the early 1930s. The present bridge is of Warren girder construction which dispenses with the need for a central pier. It is of interest that there are a number of stone sleeper blocks littering the river bed at this point, suggesting that the pier which was damaged had been constructed with old material from the original W&PR trackbed when the line was reconstructed in 1845.

26. Bridge no.47. This view shows flood damage sustained in the early 1930s, after which it was rebuilt with a Warren girder to give a clear span across the river and avoid further problems. *J. F. Addyman collection*

27. Bridge no.48. Another of the 1845 replacements which has survived the ravages of occasional flash flooding of the river Esk. *Author*

Bridge No.48

Two spans of 39 feet each. OS map ref. 847067

The last of the four cast-iron girder bridges on central stone piers of 1845, the girders being replaced in the 1880s with wrought iron.

Bridge No.49

(Was a cattle creep – now abolished)

Bridge No.50

Two spans of 50 feet each. OS map ref. 855070

This timber bridge[51] also lasted until rebuilt by Cabry in the late 1860s with wrought-iron girders supported in mid river by four cast-iron columns on cast-iron piles.

28. Bridge no.50. With nos 51 and 52, this bridge is one of a group of three which replaced timber structures in the 1860s. *Author*

29. Bridge no.51.
Author

30 Bridge no.52. *Author*

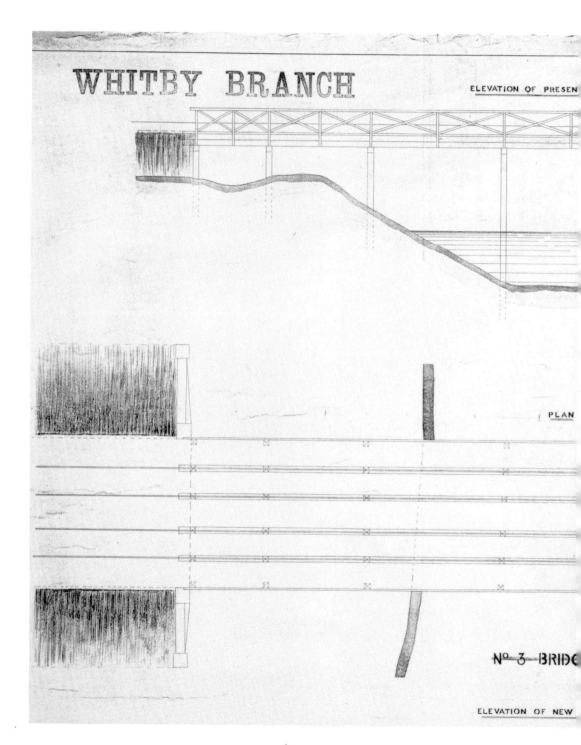

WHITBY BRANCH

ELEVATION OF PRESEN

PLAN

Nº 3 BRID

ELEVATION OF NEW

31. A portion of an engineer's drawing of Bridge no.52 showing the original timber viaduct which was replaced by an iron bridge in the late 1860s. *Dunbar Collection BR York*

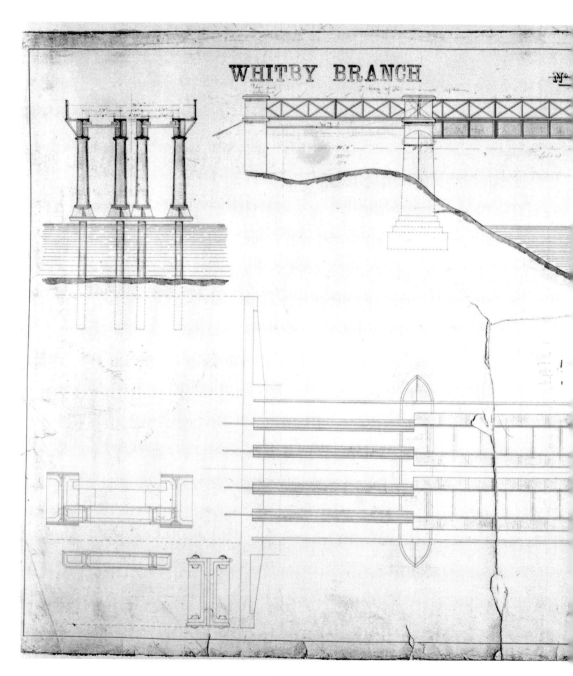

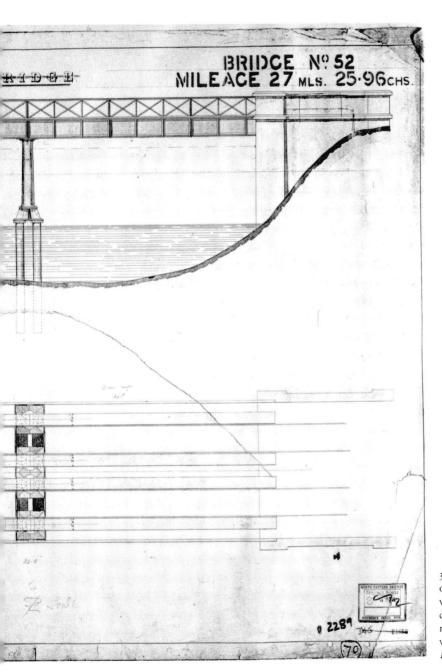

32. The engineer's drawing of Bridge no.52 showing the wrought-iron girders and cast-iron columns which replaced the earlier timber viaduct. *Dunbar Collection BR York*

33. Bridge no.53. Built in 1857 across a beck flowing into the river Esk at Sleights. Alterations to the abutments, probably made during the 1881 rebuild, and the supporting struts added in 1908 can be clearly seen. *Author*

Bridge No.51

Two spans of 50 feet each. OS map ref. 861074

The history of this bridge is believed to be similar to that of bridge no.50. The present bridge is also of wrought-iron girders supported in mid river by four cast-iron columns on cast-iron piles.

Bridge No.52

Two main spans of 50 feet each. OS map ref. 863076

This timber bridge[52] was also rebuilt in the late 1860s with wrought-iron girders supported by one stone abutment on the north bank of the river and a central pier of four cast-iron columns on cast-iron piles.

Bridge No.53

(At Sleights)

Span 47 feet. OS map ref. 868081

The original timber bridge was washed away in August 1857 [53] and Cabry submitted a plan for renewal, apparently with cast-iron girders and stone abutments.[54] The present wrought-iron girders were installed in 1881[55] and are now supported by struts added in 1908.[56] This bridge crosses a beck flowing into the river Esk.

Bridge No.54

(Small stone bridge over a beck)

Bridge No.55

(Ruswarp Viaduct)

Eleven spans of 30 feet each. OS map ref. 889090

The earlier timber structure was replaced by a wrought-iron bridge supported by ten rows of four cast-iron columns in 1869. These columns are similar in design to those of the Malton bridge.

Bridlington–Seamer line

(Opened in stages 1846/7)

No structures of note. However, eleven small timber bridges were replaced in the late 1850s.[57]

34 Bridge no.55. This long low viaduct at Ruswarp was the last of the Esk Valley bridges to be rebuilt and was completed in 1869. The balustrade is of another style common on the former NER – see Hutton and Ripon viaducts and bridges nos 45, 50, 51 and 52 on the Esk Valley line. *Author*

35. An underside view of Ruswarp Viaduct. The piers should be compared with those at Malton (FIG 21), completed in the same year. *Author*

Various engineering matters arose in the 1860s, one of which was the widening of the old Leeds & Selby Railway tunnel at Marsh Lane, Leeds, in connection with the opening of the line from Church Fenton to Micklefield on 1 April 1869. This new line gave a much quicker and more direct route between York and Leeds and made use of the old L&SR route, which had been relegated to a very secondary role by Hudson 25 years earlier when the L&SR had been leased by the Y&NMR. Consideration was in fact given to opening out the tunnel in 1865[58] but this did not occur until the early 1890s when the route was further widened to four tracks. The tunnel had been opened by the L&SR on 22 September 1834 and was built to take double track; however the width was only 22 feet.[59] It was therefore decided to increase this by five feet by taking down and rebuilding the side walls, leaving the original crown of the arch in place. As a large proportion of the ground through which it passed was either old coal workings or disintegrated shale, serious difficulties were encountered and reconstruction work took nearly two years, during which time traffic was worked through the tunnel on a single line.[60] Work began on widening the tunnel early in 1866[61] and, on 19 January, Cabry had reported to the board: [62]

You are aware of the alteration which is now being made in Marsh Lane Tunnel by widening it, this work is of a rather dangerous character, progress is slow. Arrangements have to be made for the safe working of the traffic.

Cabry was eventually able to report on 27 January 1868 that the work had been completed without accident or interruption to traffic.[63] His recommendation that the track in the tunnel should be relaid with steel rails, which were coming into use at the time, was adopted.[64]

Some years earlier, Cabry had been experimenting with steel-headed rails and 50 tons had been ordered from the Bolton Iron & Steel Company. He had reported to the board in 1862 on the results of experiments in case-hardening of rail surfaces.[65] The process involved straightening the rails and a small proportion did break at this point in the operation. The engineers Isaac Dodds and his son Thomas Weatherburn Dodds, iron founders of Rotherham, had approached the NER in 1858 offering to sell their patent process for the case hardening of wrought-iron rails.[66] By the use of a new design of furnace they were able to treat a specific depth of the rail surface by the addition of carbon and other chemicals, the heat being controlled by an elaborate system of dampers. The treated rails were then passed through rollers, whilst still hot, to apply pressure to the running surface and achieve the necessary degree of case-hardening; a process known as *cementation*. About 100 miles of the NER main line were laid with rails treated by this process[67] and the chief engineer, T. E. Harrison, had reported to the locomotive committee that further such rails had been tried out at Newcastle for six months on points and crossings and no wear had taken place. He therefore recommended that all future rails laid should be subjected to the Dodds' process and that four furnaces should be built in each of the two divisions of the NER. This would enable 6,000 tons of rails per year to be treated, the carbon necessary to the process being derived from the burning of old sleepers.[68] The NER negotiated the use of the process under licence and, in April 1859, Bourne, the Northern Division engineer, presented plans for the furnaces to the locomotive committee.[69] Rather surprisingly, T. W. Dodds did not in fact patent this method of treatment until 1865[70] although the 'patent process' was being offered to the NER seven years earlier. As this excessive hardening of the rail surface led to breakages the practice was abandoned after a few years.[71] The useful life of the patent must therefore have been a short one. In fact Bessemer had produced a method of making steel more cheaply in 1856. However this was a ductile and relatively weak steel which was less suitable for rails than the improved material which became available some fifteen years later when steel rails were to come into widespread use.[72] The original Bessemer steel was also relatively expensive which is why experiments were made with hardening the surface of rails to combine the superior wearing properties of the steel with the cheapness of wrought iron.

The question of whether or not to creosote sleepers received a good deal of attention in 1867. On the Southern Division of the NER creosoting by the Bethell process was carried out at the works at Milford, built in 1850, and by 1865 all the lines in the division had been relaid with treated sleepers.[73] However Cabry now considered that the process damaged the fibres of the timber and the life of the treated sleepers was not as long as had been expected. He did not therefore believe it was worth the extra expenditure to creosote sleepers and since September 1866 he had discontinued the process.[74] Harrison wrote to the locomotive committee on 5 December 1867[75] after consulting reports submitted by both Bourne (for the Northern Division) and Cabry. He disagreed with the latter's views stressing the importance of the choice of timber and pointing out that in his opinion Scotch Fir was preferable to Baltic timber. He quoted a number of official reports which indicated quite conclusively that the creosoting process not only preserved the timber but also increased its resistance both to crushing and breaking. He felt Cabry's experiments had not been wide ranging enough, that he had selected only the best examples of untreated sleepers and the worst of those treated to make his point, and that these results could not be taken to represent the full picture. Baltic timber was cheaper but tended to split and if the creosoting process was carried out when the timber was not perfectly dry damage could result. He therefore recommended that creosoted Scotch Fir be used whenever possible and that uncreosoted sleepers should only be used in exceptional circumstances.

Thomas Cabry's last years

AFTER nearly 35 years in the service of the NER and its predecessor, the Y&NMR, and having reached the age of 69, Cabry showed signs of wishing to retire in June 1870 due to advancing years and failing health. The board of directors persuaded him to stay on a little longer however and he finally left the railway service at end of June 1871.[76] On his retirement he was presented with a gratuity of £1,000 and a first-class pass over the NER for life.[77] A large number of his former colleagues and the staff under his control presented him with an elegant epergne and a gold-mounted ivory-headed walking stick at a presentation at his home on The Mount on 28 February 1872. Mrs Cabry was given a gold bracelet studded with precious stones. Thomas Cabry's career had begun on the Stockton & Darlington Railway, and his retirement within a few months of those of Captain William O'Brien the general manager and John Cleghorn the secretary of the NER marked the end of an era.

Bourne, the engineer of the Northern Division for many years, had also left early in 1870 on the grounds of continued ill health.[78] As Tomlinson puts it: 'With the year 1872 we enter upon the modern period of our history' – this was of course written in 1914.

Some six months after his retirement, on 9 December 1871, Cabry met George Hudson for the last time on York station. The *Yorkshire Gazette* reported later that:

…a friendship was formed between Mr Hudson and Mr Cabry which, through all the chances and changes of above 30 years, was maintained throughout. We were present at the interview between these worthy men at York Railway Station on Saturday 9th December, 1871 when Mr Hudson was suffering from serious illness and was making his way to London where he died the following Thursday. We well remember the intense feeling of these friends at their last interview – impressed as they were that it was their final opportunity of holding converse on this earth.[79]

Hudson had been on a round of visits to old friends in the York area and had been staying with J. L. Foster, a staunch supporter who was now the proprietor of the *Yorkshire Gazette,* when worsening attacks of angina forced him to return to London where a week later he had a heart attack and died.[80] Hudson's funeral was in York and many of his old allies were present. Cabry was one of the faithful few who accompanied the coffin to its final resting place at Scrayingham, north east of York.

After just over two years of retirement Thomas Cabry died peacefully at his home on Friday 5 September 1873 of diabetes and was buried in Acomb churchyard, near York, on Tuesday 9 September. His widow Margaret lived on in York until 19 May 1887 and was buried in the same grave as her husband.

Thomas Cabry left several properties to his wife including the house in The Mount, another in Mount Parade and stables in The Crescent. He also held the lease of a farm near Harrogate which he left to two of his cousins. All this in addition to a substantial sum of money in various stocks (including £11,000 in North Eastern Railway Consolidated Stock) indicating that he died a comparatively wealthy man, well-known and respected in the city of York which he had made his home for many years.

CHAPTER SEVEN

The Cabry Family

THE CABRY family's connection with the Wirral, which had begun when Joseph and his family moved there in the early nineteenth century, was to be maintained for more than a century and a half.

Catherine, one of Thomas Cabry's younger sisters, married John Maylor, a blacksmith and publican of the Old Red Lion at Willaston near Neston, in 1837. Thomas's brother Joseph also became a publican, being the landlord of the Wheatsheaf in Ness from about 1829,[1] having married in about 1825. By the time of the 1861 Census (of which he was the enumerator for Ness) he was also running a small farm of about 50 acres. Joseph and his wife Ann had seven children, and their four sons, Joseph, Henry, Charles and Thomas, all became railway employees. Their eldest daughter Mary Jane was married at Neston on 27 May 1857 to John Green, a farmer from Ness. The last of their many children lived in Ness until 1963 when he died at the age of 96.

Old Joseph, Thomas Cabry's father (grandfather of the four brothers referred to above) moved to York shortly after his wife Mary's death at Neston in January 1847. He lived in a lodging house in Mount Parade, quite close to Thomas who was living in nearby Holgate Road, and remained there until his death on 16 September 1858 at the age of 86. The lady who ran the establishment, which was mostly occupied by railway employees, was Ann Whitehead. There is a slight mystery about her identity as old Joseph is described in the 1851 Census records as her father, and Henry Cabry (junior), who was living in the same house, as her nephew. However Ann Whitehead's age is given as 55 so she

would have been born before Joseph's marriage in 1798 and a list of immediate members of Joseph's family (in the possession of one of his descendants) signed by one of his daughters, Catherine, and dated 1857, only mentions one 'Ann', a niece of Joseph's wife Mary who was born in 1794. It seems likely therefore that Ann Whitehead was Joseph's niece by marriage and that the Census records must be incorrect in this instance.

Henry Cabry (junior)

HENRY was 18 at the time of the 1851 Census and described as a clerk on the York & North Midland Railway but was appointed as traffic manager of the Blyth & Tyne Railway, in Northumberland, in January 1862 at an annual salary of £275.[2] He only stayed in the job for just over three years and resigned in September 1865.[3] History does not record the reason for his resignation but ill health may have been the cause. He was unmarried and living with his father Joseph at Ness at the time of the 1871 census, dying on 8 December of that year aged only 38.

Thomas Cabry (junior)

THE youngest of the four brothers, Thomas was born in 1842 and had also left his home in Ness by the time of the 1861 Census. He was also working in the North Eastern Railway's engineer's office at York by 1863, when his annual salary was increased to £100.[4] He was still with the NER in 1865 but is not referred to again in the company records. He married in 1869 and died in 1882 at the early age of 40.

36. Young Henry Cabry – Thomas Cabry's nephew, taken in Brussels. *Weber family collection*

Charles Cabry

CHARLES had left his home in Ness by the time of the 1851 Census when he was 16 but the first reference to him in NER records does not appear until 1860 when his annual salary in the engineer's office was increased to £130.[5] He became outdoor assistant in 1869[6] and succeeded Thomas Cabry (senior) in 1871.

When he succeeded his uncle as engineer of the Southern Division,[7] he only held the position for 3½ years, resigning with effect from 30 November 1874.[8] It is not clear why his period in office was so short as he had worked his way up through the engineer's department where he had been since at least 1860 and was only 39 at the time of his resignation. Shortly after his appointment he had been elected a member of the Institution of Mechanical Engineers but resigned on 24 December 1878. At this time he was living at 19 The Mount, quite close to Thomas Cabry's old house.[9] He was one of the many guests at the banquet held to commemorate the 50th anniversary of the Stockton & Darlington Railway in September 1875 and he married Jane Judson at Ripon Cathedral in 1880. He died on 24 January 1900 at the age of 64 and from the contents of his will it appears he and his wife were running a coaching inn in Knaresborough. His wife came from a family which was in this line of business, giving her address as the Royal Hotel, West Hartlepool at the time her marriage. In 1885 the NER estate agent, George Irving, reported to the board that the lease of this hotel had just expired and it was resolved that it should be 'let or leased as Mrs Cabry the present tenant may prefer'.[10] This would seem to indicate that she continued to run the establishment at least until 1885. Mrs Cabry lived in the Knaresborough district until her death in Harrogate in 1909.

Joseph Cabry (junior)

JOSEPH Cabry was born at Ness in about 1831, the eldest of the four brothers. By the age of 10 he was living with his grandparents (Joseph and Mary) at Little Neston Colliery whereas the rest of his family were living at nearby Ness. He was at first employed under Thomas Cabry at York but in August 1853 he was appointed resident engineer on the Midland Great Western Railway in Ireland.[11]

At the end of his period of notice on the Y&NMR a farewell party was held for him at the Elephant & Castle in Skeldergate, York on 16 November 1853 when after a convivial evening he was presented by his colleagues with an instrument case.[12] The Elephant & Castle was run by a former Y&NMR engine driver Ralph Watkin who by coincidence had been one of the witnesses called by John Gray in the valve gear arbitration case two years previously.[13]

Edward Wilson, Joseph Cabry's predecessor on the MGWR, had also come from Y&NMR where he had been the 'Engine and Locomotive Superintendent at York'[14] since 1847, having previously been employed on the Hull & Selby Railway.[15] He had charge of the MGWR Locomotive Department from November 1853.[16] Wilson obtained the position of locomotive superintendent of the Oxford, Worcester & Wolverhampton Railway and his resignation from the MGWR was minuted on 14 August 1856. Cabry's appointment as Wilson's successor is not mentioned in the company minutes but in fact he was in office by 25 October 1856. Wilson's locomotive assistant was John Kershaw who is only known on the MGWR by a press report of May 1855 regarding a presentation to him on 'going as locomotive superintendent to the Great Indian Peninsula Railway'. Cabry must therefore have assisted only on the civil engineering side until Kershaw's departure and would have been an obvious choice as successor to Wilson in 1856. He seems to have taken over without formality as the headings in the MGWR board minute books change from 'On Mr Wilson's Reports' to 'On Mr Cabry's Reports' without comment in late 1856.

Joseph Cabry returned briefly to Neston to marry Margaret Day on 5 July 1855 and remained on the MGWR until 1862 when his resignation was minuted on 25 September at which time the civil and mechanical engineering departments were separated. However it would seem that he may have left under a cloud as a report of a shareholders' committee meeting in 1865 stated that:

It was also proved that a very objectionable system, in letting expensive contracts for rolling stock and permanent way materials, without sufficient competition, prevailed for some time, prior to 1862, which gave rise to grave charges of official corruption, and necessitated the retirement of one of the leading

37. Charles Cabry, taken in Brussels.
Weber family collection

Officers from the Company's service, and the transfer of the Stores Department to the charge of the Secretary…[17]

This must be taken to refer to Joseph Cabry's resignation although a further press report at the time of his departure in 1862 stated that he was leaving the MGWR to go to the Waterford & Limerick Railway. There was however no such vacancy on that railway which was an impecunious concern boasting a locomotive stock of only 27, whereas the MGWR was a much larger line with 60 locomotives on its books. If this was an attempt by Cabry to disguise his dismissal it was inept, as he could easily have said he was going to another post in England or elsewhere which would have been much harder to verify. Apparently such a drastic course of action as dismissal in these circumstances was very rare. A late-Victorian railway manager, Joseph Tatlow, was with the MGWR for a number of years from 1890 and could only remember two other such instances on British or Irish railways during his long career.[18]

Joseph Cabry introduced three classes of locomotive to the MGWR, an 0-4-2 of 1860 built by Fairbairn, a 2-2-2 of 1862 by Hawthorn and an 0-4-2 (a popular wheel arrangement in Ireland at the time) in 1863 built by Neilson's to Cabry's own design. The Hawthorn singles had 6'6" driving wheels, 4'3" carrying wheels and cylinders of 15"x22". They had double sandwich frames with outside bearings to all wheels and additional inside bearings for the driving wheels: six being supplied to the MGWR.[19] There were sufficient similarities in design between these three types to indicate that Cabry at least provided the builders with an outline drawing of what he wanted in addition to a written specification.

Although no patent specification can be found, an invention known as 'Cabry & Owen's Patent Tyre Fastening' is referred to in the Board of Trade Inspector's report of an accident near Sittingbourne on the London, Chatham & Dover Railway on 4 February 1861, caused by a broken wheel tyre on the leading van of a Canterbury to Victoria train.[20] This tyre was supplied by Sandford and Owen of Rotherham and Captain Tyler, the inspector, gave examples of a number of different tyre fixing methods in use at the time. He said that the wheel-set which contained the defective tyre was stamped 'Owen's patent' and that the method was superior to some others as the tyre was made in one piece and therefore avoided the inherent weakness of a welded joint. However he criticised the rivets used to secure the tyre to the wheel which were yet another source of weakness. The 'Cabry and Owen' fastening was similar to the others mentioned in the report but the exact method of fixing the tyre to the wheel differed slightly and Captain Tyler:

…feared that in this system the dovetailed surfaces might not in all cases be fitted with sufficient accuracy to ensure a good result; and that, even if they did so in the first instance, the tyre might alter its shape as it became thin from wear, to an extent that would destroy the efficiency of the fastening.

This fastening was just one of a number being experimented with at a time when broken tyres were becoming a problem.

After his departure from the MGWR Joseph Cabry spent some time in London. He was living at 39 Marylebone Road, the address of a sculptor named Samuel Edmund Harrison in 1863 and in the following year his address was given as 3 Colbeck Terrace, Tynemouth.[21] In October 1865

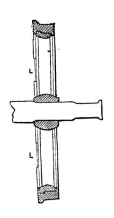
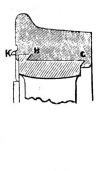

38. The Cabry & Owen tyre fastening. From Captain Tyler's report into an incident near Sittingbourne on 4 February 1861 involving the breakage of a tyre on the leading van. *Public Record Office*

39. The Neilson 0-4-2 locomotive built to Joseph Cabry's specification in 1863. It was one of six supplied to the Midland Great Western Railway of Ireland, works nos 937–942. *North British Locomotive Collection. By courtesy of the Mitchell Library, Glasgow*

he accepted the position of manager of the Blyth & Tyne Railway.[22] This position combined the duties of engineer and manager and was a definite step down from his situation on the MGWR, the B&TR being an altogether smaller mainly coal-carrying concern with a far lower route mileage than the Irish line and with only 25 locomotives in 1863, a figure which had risen to 35 by 1868/9.[23] His appointment may not have been without family influence, his younger brother Henry having held the same position before him, and in 1856 the advice of his uncle, Thomas Cabry, had been sought in connection with the arrangement of the new workshops then being built at Percy Main. Thomas Cabry's various suggestions were adopted and he received a fee of £15 15s for 'Engineering advice'.[24]

The Blyth & Tyne was amalgamated with the NER on 7 August 1874 and Joseph Cabry continued as passenger superintendent, also having charge of the permanent way of the B&TR section, until 1883.[25] At the final meeting of the old B&TR board

on 31 August 1874 £1,000 was set aside to present silver plate to the secretary, manager and engineer for their services to the Company.[26] Joseph obviously treasured this plate as he left it to his widow for her use during her lifetime only, thereafter to be passed on to his grandson and down through the family.

He was appointed as engineer of the Central Division of the NER on 5 April 1883[27] and his annual salary increased to £850 (this was further raised to £1,000 on 1 May 1884). His former B&TR duties were divided between the various Northern Division departments concerned.

On 24 August 1887 Cabry took out a patent for steel sleepers, jointly with a colleague W. H. Kinch who was the engineer's assistant at Darlington. The patent sleepers incorporated jaws, in place of chairs, to hold flat-bottomed rails and were a one-piece steel pressing, the desired inward tilt of the rail being obtained by pressing up only the portion of the sleeper directly beneath the rail.

This avoided what was considered the objectionable practice of bending the sleeper up from the centre and allowed the Cabry & Kinch sleeper to be laid flat thus preventing transverse movement in the ballast. The rail was held in position with a wedge-shaped steel split key inserted under the inner jaw of the sleeper. Studs were placed on each side of the outer jaw both to assist in keeping the track to gauge and to relieve the jaw of outward pressure. It was claimed that the first cost of this type of track compared favourably with conventional wooden sleepers and chairs, and that there would be a considerable saving on maintenance.[28]

Various types of iron and steel sleepers had been used as far back as 1849[29] and the longest and most extensive trial had been on the London & North Western Railway with Francis Webb's patent all-steel track. With this system, chairs were attached to the sleepers so that standard bull-head rail could be used. The NER had tried out a one-mile length of track laid with wrought-iron sleepers in 1878[30] and in 1886 they experimented with a steel sleeper

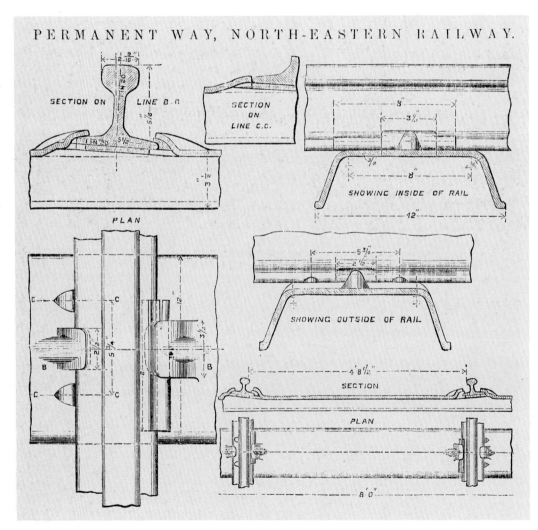

40. The Cabry & Kinch patent steel sleeper. *'The Engineer', 4 January 1889*

41. Joseph Cabry (seated front row centre) with members of his engineering staff. W.H. Kinch is seated to his right.
Public Record Office (RAIL 1021/96)

design by Riley.[31] In 1888 the NER way & works committee authorised a limited trial of the Cabry and Kinch sleepers. 1,000 tons of flat-bottomed rails with an appropriate quantity of patent sleepers were ordered from Bolckow, Vaughan & Co. in October 1888[32] and approximately 1,020 yards were laid in the Northern Division at Benwell on both the up and down lines, a length also being laid on the up line near Durham. The patent sleeper was not a success however and these stretches of track were taken up in August 1894 and replaced by wooden sleepers with the usual bull-head rail, the steel sleepers having 'so generally failed' after only six years in use.[33] The main problem with steel sleepers in general was that they were not heavy enough, nor did they possess a sufficient lateral bearing surface to maintain track alignment within

the tolerances required for high speed operation. Steel sleepers also corroded badly in ill-drained ballast. They were successfully used in drier climates overseas where axle loads and train speeds were lower. Scarcity of timber and the action of termites were also important factors.

When the Engineer-in-Chief of the NER, T. E. Harrison, died in office in 1888 the company decided not to replace him or appoint a consulting engineer but to reorganise the divisions. According to the board minutes[34] Alfred Harrison was appointed engineer of the re-arranged Northern Division and Joseph Cabry that of the enlarged Central Division where he remained until his retirement in 1891.[35] He died in Newcastle on Friday 22 October 1897, at the age of 65, after a period of failing health.[36]

42. Opening of the first Belgian Railway 'Premier train au départ de L'allée Vert 1835'.
Anonymous aquarelle – Musée Communal de Bruxelles

CHAPTER EIGHT

Henry Cabry

Henry Cabry was born at Percy Main in the parish of Tynemouth in Northumberland on 5 June 1805.[1] As a boy he worked with his father and two elder brothers at the Jimmy pit at Killingworth, as described earlier and is mentioned in the letter from George Stephenson to Henry's father Joseph dated 2 March 1820, which is referred to in chapter one:

Henry at his old job – he is also very attentive at school and gets forward very well – he is now a very good arithmetician and is at present learning Measuration in which he makes good progress.[2]

Henry joined Robert Stephenson & Co., probably in late 1823 or early 1824, because we know he was employed at their Newcastle factory[3] and was involved with the building of the Stockton & Darlington Railway.[4] In due course he was recruited as locomotive superintendent of the Leicester & Swannington Railway, probably being sent there with the first locomotive, the *Comet.* It was the practice of Robert Stephenson & Co. to send a mechanic with the locomotives they delivered to set them in working order on site and such men were not infrequently recruited to the staff of the company concerned to take charge of the engines.[5] The *Comet* was despatched by sea in late April 1832 and arrived at Leicester by canal in time for the opening of the first section of the L&S on 5 May 1832.[6] Trouble was experienced with this and subsequent engines delivered as they were not powerful enough to keep pace with the expanding traffic on the line.[7] Against this background Henry Cabry must have had a difficult time keeping the traffic moving and evidently did not satisfy his employers. He was dismissed by the directors on 15 January 1834, with a week's wages in lieu of notice, after the manager, Ashlin Bagster, 'represented that Henry Cabrey the overlooker of the locomotive engines has been guilty of repeated negligence and when remonstrated with was insolent towards him'.[8]

Presumably he then returned to Newcastle as he was sent to Belgium in 1835 by George Stephenson, probably with one of the first locomotives delivered from Robert Stephenson & Co. to the State Railways. Three engines were ordered by the Belgian government but one of them had to be sub-contracted to the Vulcan Foundry, near Warrington, owing to pressure of work at Newcastle. The Stephenson locomotives were named *La Flêche* and *Stephenson,* whilst the third, from the Vulcan Foundry, was called *L'Elephant.* The first section of the Belgian State Railways between Brussels and Mechlin was opened on 6 May 1835 and the first train was driven by an English driver,[9] possibly Cabry himself.

By a royal order of 24 July 1837[10] Cabry was appointed 'Chief Mechanic and Engineer of the Belgian State Railways' which title in fact referred to his position as chief superintendent of the Eastern lines, based in Brussels. George Stephenson, in his speech at the partial opening of the York & North Midland Railway in 1839 said that Henry Cabry had 'given great satisfaction to the King and his ministers and, although the son of a poor man, had married a lady of fortune and was possessed of some influence'.[11]

On 21 August 1838 Henry Cabry was in the news: a special train hauled by the locomotive No.5

43. Fanny Cabry. *Weber Family Collection*

first iron bridge in Belgium, at the Château de Bazel, in 1824.[13]

It was not surprising, perhaps, that Henry Cabry married into an engineering family. Apart from his father-in-law, two engineers who were regarded as major figures in the construction of the Belgian Railways were also members of the Vifquain family. Pierre Simons was a son-in-law of Jean-Baptiste Vifquain having married Antonia-Zoé Georges, one of two daughters of his wife France-Louise by her first marriage. Gustave de Ridder married the other daughter, Armande. These girls were of course half sisters-in-law of Henry Cabry.[14] Simons and de Ridder also assisted Vifquain with the construction of the Brussels– Charleroi canal.[15]

In a little more than a year after their marriage Henry and Elizabeth-Mathilde produced a daughter, Marie-Louise, who was born on 7 April 1840. She was always known as Fanny and by all accounts was a talented young lady. She was an accomplished artist and a number of charming watercolours of various plants and flowers are in the possession of the Weber family, descendants of her son Maurice Weber, who still live in Brussels and kept in touch with descendants of the Cabrys in the Wirral until the 1960s. Fanny died giving birth to her second child (who also died) on 8 June 1873 at the early age of 33.

Henry Cabry was the most innovative member of his family and designed several devices. The most important of which was a locomotive valve gear. He also invented a brake carriage and is credited with the invention of a steam trumpet.

As the operation of valve gears can be somewhat difficult to understand it may be of help to explain the historical background to Henry Cabry's invention and its place in their development.

Early valve gears

THE earliest locomotives had no valve gear as we would understand it today. They did not exploit the expansive properties of steam, due in part to low boiler pressures, and required only a means of reversing. Ignoring the primitive period, steam admission and exhaust was controlled by a reciprocating slide valve driven by an *eccentric* keyed to the crank axle. Sometimes there was but one eccentric per cylinder, mounted loose on the axle and driven by a pin engaging in a curved slot

Eclair, which was returning the King of the Belgians to Bruges after a visit to Ostend, was derailed on the bridge over the river Leie at Ghent and the engine was thrown into the water. The driver and fireman were killed and Cabry, caught between the engine and the tender, was seriously injured.[12] His left leg was crushed and his forthcoming marriage to Elizabeth-Mathilde Vifquain was delayed until he had fully recovered, the wedding eventually taking place on 14 March 1839. Henry Cabry's bride was born in Brussels, the daughter of Jean-Baptiste Vifquain, a well known civil engineer in Belgium.

Vifquain is principally remembered as a town planner but he also surveyed and supervised the construction of the Brussels–Charleroi canal between 1827 and 1832. He later made a study of the Belgian canal network and carried out many improvements. Vifquain was also responsible for bringing the railway into the centre of Brussels, some years after the original terminus had been built on the outskirts of the city, and built the

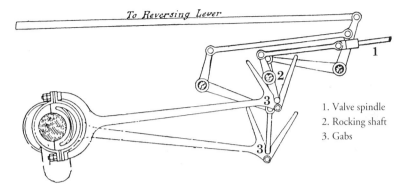

1. Valve spindle
2. Rocking shaft
3. Gabs

44. Gab gear as used by Robert Stephenson & Co. in 1838. Two weighshafts are connected to the reversing lever so that one gab or the other is engaged with the rocking shaft according to the direction of motion.

in the eccentric disc, the pin being mounted either on one cheek of the crank or on a separate disc keyed to the axle. The ends of the slot corresponded to the correct angular positions for forward and reverse running, the locomotive being reversed by moving it a short distance in the opposite direction whereupon the pin moved round to the opposite end of the slot – such an eccentric is known as a *slip eccentric*. More often there were two eccentrics for each cylinder, one for forward gear and the other for reverse.

With slip eccentric gear, reversing was accomplished by disconnecting the valves from their eccentrics and working them by hand to move the locomotive backwards, reconnecting the gear once the eccentric had reversed itself. With fixed eccentrics, the valve was disconnected from one and connected to the other. It sounds simple but there was a catch: the original means of connecting and disconnecting the eccentric rods was by means of a cup and stud coupling – for example the end of the eccentric rod might have a semicircular cup that fitted over a matching pin on one end of a rocking lever that drove the valve spindle. The two fitted together snugly with minimum backlash and disengaged readily but they would only *engage* if they were exactly in line, which entailed juggling the valves and/or locomotive until the gear dropped in. Needless to say, each valve spindle had to be connected to a handle on the footplate whereby the valve could be 'handed' while carrying out this juggling act, handles which flailed about all the time

the locomotive was in motion. The best practical illustration of this primitive form of reversing gear is the reproduction Liverpool & Manchester Railway *Planet* constructed by the Museum of Science and Industry in Manchester, commissioned in 1993.

The first step towards a modern valve gear was made in 1833/34 with a very simple modification to the semicircular cup just described, namely the provision of a V-shaped extension the open end of which was several times wider than the diameter of the stud. The sloping cheeks of this entry flare could therefore pick up the stud and guide it into the cup, eliminating the need for the two parts to be exactly in line and greatly simplifying the whole operation. Not unnaturally, these beak-like devices were known as *gabs* and valve gears employing them by the generic term *gab gear*.

The next step, following immediately upon the first, was to standardise on two eccentrics per cylinder and connect all the eccentric rods to a lever on the footplate whereby reversing could be accomplished simply by disengaging one pair of gabs and simultaneously engaging the other. This being possible without needing to 'hand' the valves, the valve handles on the footplate were eliminated, together with their attendant linkage, to produce the definitive gab gear used by the majority of locomotive builders during the next decade, when most locomotives had valves above the cylinders driven through a rocking shaft. Being half of a disconnectable joint, the gabs could be mounted either on the ends of the eccentric rod or

Slide valve events
with and without lap

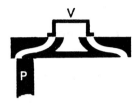

FIG 45

FIG 46

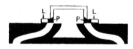

FIG 47

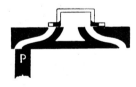

FIG 48

PRIMARY COMPONENT OF TRAVEL

FIG.45 shows a simple slide valve without lap V at the mid-point of its travel, covering both steam ports, while the piston P is at the end of its stroke. V is driven by an eccentric whose angular position is represented by E, in this case at right angles to the crank C which is rotating clockwise. V is about to admit steam behind P, driving it to the right. In FIG.46 the crank has rotated through 90° bringing the piston to mid-stroke and the valve to the extreme right-hand end of its travel. The primary component of travel is the throw of E, i.e twice the distance that the valve has moved between FIG.45 and FIG.46.

LAP

FIG.47 shows a valve with lap. The solid part of each face P corresponds to the whole face of the valve shown in FIGS.45 and 46 and is the same width as the steam port. The additional open part of each face L which overlaps the port is the *lap*, also known in Cabry's time as the *cover*.

SECONDARY COMPONENT OF TRAVEL

FIG.48 shows the same valve as in FIG.47 about to admit steam with the crank on dead centre. To do so it must be moved right from a central position by an amount equal to the lap, which is done by advancing the eccentric E to position E^1, through angle A. In practice, the eccentric is usually advanced slightly further (E^2 so that the valve opens to steam just before the piston reaches the end of its stroke. The amount by which the valve has opened at the end of the stroke is the *lead* and the total amount by which the valve has been displaced from centre (lap + lead) is the *advance* and the angle through which the eccentric has been moved forward from its original position at right angles to the crank is the *angle of advance*. The secondary component of travel is twice the advance.

on the rocking shaft and FIG.44 shows the commoner form with gabs on the eccentric rods. The Cabry gear had the forward gab, sometimes both, on the rocking shaft.

To understand the nuances of Henry Cabry's valve gear it is necessary first to appreciate the importance of the *angle of advance,* most readily explained by considering a simple non-reversible engine in which the slide valve is driven directly by an eccentric keyed to the crankshaft and arranged to cut off steam before the end of the stroke: in other words, working with a small but fixed degree of expansion. A slide valve leads the piston, that is the valve is somewhere in the middle of its travel when the piston reaches the end of its stroke and begins to move back in the same direction as the valve. A plain valve with faces exactly the same width as the ports – which cannot provide any degree of expansion – would in fact be half-way through its travel and about to open to steam as the piston reached the end of its stroke: such a valve could therefore be driven by an eccentric set exactly ninety degrees in advance of the crank having a throw equal to half the valve travel. The motion produced by such an eccentric is exactly the same as the *primary component of travel* of a valve gear giving variable expansion and having the same maximum valve travel.

To provide a degree of expansion by making the valve cut off before the end of the stroke, the faces of the valve are widened so that they overlap the steam ports when centralised – the extra length beyond the edge of the port being known as the *lap.* In order that the valve will still open to steam at the right point, it must therefore travel further by an amount equal to the lap by the time the piston arrives at the end of its stroke, which is achieved by moving the eccentric forward to provide the extra travel: this in turn closes the valve earlier and provides the required cut-off. The amount by which the angle between the crank and the eccentric exceeds ninety degrees is termed the *angle of advance* and the resultant displacement of the valve from a central position at the commencement of the stroke, equal to the lap, is half the *secondary component of valve travel.*

In practice, the secondary component is slightly greater than twice the lap so that the valve has just opened to steam as the piston reverses, this opening

being termed the *lead.* It is provided to control compression at the end of the exhaust stroke and to ensure that full pressure is available in the cylinder at the commencement of the power stroke.

To provide variable cut-off, it is necessary to vary the primary component of valve travel without significantly altering the secondary component.

Henry Cabry's valve gear in Belgium

HENRY Cabry's 'Long Fork' valve gear was patented in Belgium on 31 July 1841.[16] In the patent specification Cabry claimed that his mechanism would vary the point of cut-off between 2/10ths and 9/10ths of the stroke and this would be achieved without the locomotive having to stop or slow down and would result in a saving in fuel of at least 25%.

FIG.49 is taken from the drawing which accompanied the patent specification. The gear is shown in the full forward position, but viewed from the side of the mechanism which shows the backward eccentric [1] disengaged from it's 'long fork' gab [2] for the sake of clarity. The corresponding stud on the forward eccentric is at the highest point in its long fork. Like the backward long fork shown, this forms the gab by which the movement, derived from the main axle by the eccentric, is transmitted to the slide valve which admits steam to the cylinder. In this position the lever [3] moves the spindle [4] to the maximum extent, allowing steam to enter the piston for 9/10ths of the stroke. As a lever on the footplate is pulled back, the stud on the forward eccentric moves down the long fork limiting the movement of the spindle and cutting off the supply of steam earlier in the stroke. The lever on the footplate was designed to engage in a series of slotted notches equally spaced in the arc of a circle to hold the gear in the desired position.

Cabry claimed simplicity, reliability and cheap and easy conversion of existing locomotives as well as economy for his invention. He also mentioned that he had another means of varying the slide valve travel but did not go into further detail. It is also plain from the specification that he intended the gear for use on all types of steam engine, not just locomotives.

Cabry's valve gear was a simple modification of

the type of gab gear having gabs fitted to the valve rockers and studs to the eccentric rods. It will be obvious that the travel of the eccentric was fixed and so therefore was that of anything mounted on the eccentric rod; to vary the valve travel it was necessary to interpose some form of variable lever between the end of the eccentric rod and the valve spindle. This Cabry did by attaching his gabs to the lower arm of the rocker and altering the cheeks so that they guided the stud into a deep slot rather than a plain cup. The inner end of this slot was the same distance from the rocker pivot as the cup of a normal gab, hence when the eccentric rod stud was drawn fully into the slot the geometry of the gear and the valve travel were unaltered. However, if the stud was held further down the slot, the effective length of the rocker arm was increased and for the

same travel of the stud the valve spindle moved a shorter distance. Cut-off being a function of valve travel, the slotted gab therefore provided a means of shortening the cut-off to increase the degree of expansion.

The major limitation of Cabry's gear was that it shortened both components of motion at once, whereas a geometrically correct gear would alter only the primary one. To maintain the secondary component while reducing the primary, the angle of advance of the eccentric must be increased, literally or effectively. In the absence of any provision for so doing, Cabry's gear did not in fact achieve as much as was popularly supposed: this appears to have been appreciated in Belgium but certain British writers seem to have imagined that reducing valve travel reduced cut-off by a corres-

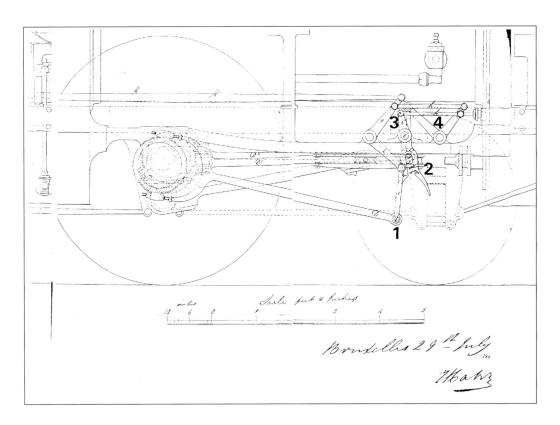

49. Part of the Belgian patent specification drawing numbered to show the parts referred to on page 79.
SNCB Archives, Mechlin

ponding amount. The author of an enthusiastic account in the *Railway Chronicle* of 27 April 1844 was very coy about it, saying that 'by a proper adjustment of lead and cover (lap), variable expansion is accomplished'. He did not explain how such adjustment might be accomplished but said that he *might* go into greater detail on a future occasion and even 'consider how perfection is to be attained'. Perhaps he had tried to work it out for himself and suddenly realised the truth.

The limited degree of expansion afforded by the gear is demonstrated by FIGS 50 and 51 which are based on diagrams in J. Goussens' biography of Egide Walschaerts, published in 1984.

Taking first the diagram for maximum valve travel, radial lines represent the position of the crank at the four cardinal points of the cycle – *Admission* (valve open to steam), *Cut-off* (valve closed to steam), *Release* (valve open to exhaust) and *Compression* (valve closed to exhaust). The perpendiculars from the end of each line to the diameter mark off the corresponding position of the piston – ignoring angularity of the connecting rod. As, however, the effect of angularity is to make things happen earlier on one stroke and correspondingly later on the other, the positions marked represent a mean position for both ends of the cylinder.

It can be seen that the valve opened to steam shortly before dead centre – the effect of a significant amount of lead – and closed well towards the end of the stroke, cut-off taking place at 85% stroke. This was the cut-off normally employed in those days. The steam was then allowed to expand until 96% stroke, when the valve opened to exhaust. On the return stroke the valve remained open to exhaust for more than three-quarters of the stroke, allowing only a short period of compression before lead steam was admitted to recommence the cycle.

Moving to the diagram for reduced valve travel, we find that admission takes place much closer to dead centre, demonstrating the reduction in lead at shorter cut-off. Moving round, a surprise awaits us, however: cut-off takes place at 81% stroke and exhaust at 96½%. To modern eyes the cut-off has not significantly been reduced, but if the claim was to have increased the degree of expansion this has in fact happened because expansion now takes place for 15½% of the stroke instead of 11%. A little more work would be

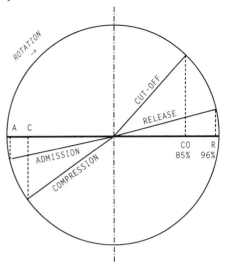

50 *(above)* Crank positions for maximum valve travel and 51 *(below)* positions for reduced valve travel.

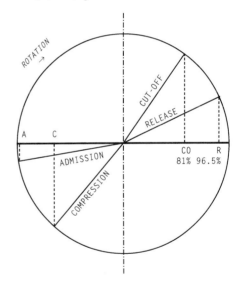

extracted from the steam, to be sure, but equally beneficial would be the softer blast resulting from the lower exhaust pressure and less rapid opening of the valve. At the opposite end of the stroke, however, compression begins much earlier and the work absorbed therein will increase. This will make the locomotive run a little more easily; it will be quieter and will probably burn less fuel.

For comparison, a modern valve gear would probably have a maximum cut-off of 75–77% and a corresponding reduction in valve travel would reduce this to something like 40%. At the latter setting, exhaust would take place earlier with a much lower pressure in the cylinder and compression would probably start a little earlier to ensure a final pressure approximating to that in the steam chest. With the same initial steam pressure the locomotive would be significantly more efficient than one with Cabry gear but its power output would be less because the mean pressure in the cylinder would be lower. One suspects that Walschaerts' biographer may have picked a poor example of Cabry gear to make his point, but even so it is clear that it did not and could not achieve the degree of expansion afforded by Stephenson or Walschaerts gear.

It is important to put things in their proper context. When Cabry designed his gear, boiler pressures were relatively low – typically 50–60 lb/sq.in. – and, apart from a small number of locomotives fitted with elaborate but mechanically unreliable 'expansion gears' (such as that devised by John Gray), most trains were hauled by relatively small locomotives with fierce exhausts whose boilers were badly proportioned for burning coke (the usual fuel). That his gear afforded a modicum of expansive working and in so doing reduced the intensity of the blast was, for its time, a step in the right direction. What is more, it achieved quantifiable improvement without resorting to mechanical complexity. Five years later much had changed as boilers were getting larger – initially through the medium of 'long-boiler' designs whose longer tubes could extract more heat from the flue gas. At the same time the greater degree of expansion made possible by the early link motions was encouraging engineers to introduce higher boiler pressures with which such expansive working could advantageously be employed.

Against this background it is easy to see why Cabry's gear attracted quite an amount of attention when first introduced. With many engineers searching for a satisfactory system of variable expansion it is not surprising that claims in favour of his relatively simple mechanism were at times exaggerated.

Of course, as chief mechanical engineer, with particular responsibility for the Eastern lines of the Belgian railways, Cabry was in a good position to

exert his influence. He was based in Brussels and Fr Fischer, through whom Egide Walschaerts obtained the first patent for his valve gear in 1844, also worked from Brussels as mechanical under-engineer of the Southern section.

Soon after patenting his valve gear Cabry approached Jean-Baptiste Masui, the Director of Railways, for authority to test the gear on some of the Belgian State Railway locomotives.[17] He agreed to the gear being fitted to two engines to enable tests to be made and these were quickly arranged by Cabry in November 1841. Further tests between Brussels and Ans (near Liège) followed, showing economies averaging 27% for locomotives fitted with Cabry's gear. The authorities, however, were sceptical and another set of tests was arranged, supervised by a board of engineers, but unfortunately held during appalling weather conditions, which produced rather inconclusive results.

Cabry had visited England at about this time and on his return to Brussels wrote to Daniel Gooch, locomotive superintendent of the Great Western Railway, in March 1842[18] that 'we have made more experiments with the Engine which has it [his valve gear] applied since I arrived hear & the result is as flattering as before' so he evidently did not share the misgivings expressed in Belgium. He also mentioned that he had shown the plans of his gear to Gooch's chief, Brunel, who had promised to adapt some GWR engines by fitting the device. From the tone of the letter it is obvious that Brunel had not communicated with Cabry, who was anxious to know whether his gear had been tried out. As Brunel had been experimenting with an expansion gear himself since 1840[19] he was probably not in fact disposed to try Cabry's gear but may merely have expressed an interest out of politeness. He was still working on his own gear in 1843[20] but, as no further references to it can be found, it seems likely that it came to nothing. The letter suggests that the Cabry gear was also patented in France, Austria and Prussia.

Another device, called an 'exhaust regulator', is referred to in Masui's report on the Belgian tests and he expressed surprise that the board of engineers had used engines with this device and with longer lap in the comparative tests against those fitted with Cabry's gear because Cabry's original trials in November 1841 had been against

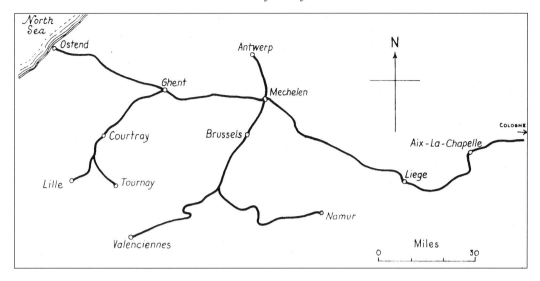

52. The Belgian Railway routes on which tests with Henry Cabry's valve gear were carried out in 1842.

ordinary engines not fitted with either of these improvements.

This exhaust regulator was probably the device known in Britain as an exhaust cock, a valve mounted at the base of the blastpipe whereby exhaust steam could be discharged directly to atmosphere below the smokebox. The object was to reduce exhaust pressure and hence the severity of the blast. A by-product of reducing exhaust pressure would be a slight increase in useful work performed in the cylinders, especially if the steam passages in the cylinder block were too small – as was so often the case. This being a similar effect to that produced by Cabry's gear, it is easy to see why a locomotive fitted with an exhaust regulator was unwelcome in a carefully staged demonstration of the former. Coincidentally, the last British railway to fit exhaust cocks as standard was Thomas Cabry's employer, the North Eastern Railway, where they survived until Edward Fletcher retired in 1882. His successor, Alexander McDonnell then began to root out what he considered to be obsolete practices.

Masui decided that the various tests, intended to prove the benefits to be derived from the gear, were merely clouding the issue but, perhaps rather surprisingly, nevertheless proposed to the Minister of Public Works that the gear should be fitted to all new engines made at the three industrial establishments in Belgium devoted to locomotive construction. He also recommended other changes which he did not specify. He concluded that yet further tests in normal service – this time not undertaken by his panel of experts – should be made against engines not fitted with the Cabry gear, extra lap or the exhaust regulator thereby returning to the conditions of Cabry's original tests which had proved so favourable for his invention. Not surprisingly, these later tests came out clearly in favour of Cabry's gear. They were conducted between 7 September and 13 October 1842 on various sections of the Belgian Railways alternating the two types of locomotive in continuous tests, achieving the following economies with the Cabry gear:

Brussels to Mechlin	(15 miles)	30%
Mechlin to Ghent	(35 miles)	43%
Brussels to Antwerp	(30 miles)	25%(approx.)
Ghent to Courtray	(25 miles)	37%

Although the greatest economy was achieved on the longest run, between Mechlin and Ghent, all four routes were fairly level and the trains heavy, not circumstances favourable to expansion, which could not be used as effectively as would have been the case if the routes had been undulating or the loads lighter. These tests were conducted many months after the earlier ones and in the interval Masui said 'a general measure, with regard to the consumption of coke, contributed to make the results more conclusive'. This refers to a bonus scheme for all drivers, those in charge of engines fitted with Cabry's gear being allowed 25% less fuel to put them on equal terms with drivers of older engines. The capacity of variable expansion to slow down steam production was said to have valuable side effects. It was believed that the reduced draught from the softer exhaust would cause less wear and tear to the firebox and boiler and would also draw fewer cinders through the boiler tubes.

After these tests were completed, Masui reported that he was convinced of the benefits of the Cabry system and asked the Minister of Public Works to authorise use of the gear on the Eastern lines and to consider its more general introduction on the remaining sections of the State Railways. Presumably, as Cabry was in charge of the Eastern section, it was a logical first choice but the more hilly nature of the lines when compared to others in Belgium may have been the deciding factor.

An official statement[21] gave the results of further comparative tests on the Ans to Mechlin line between a locomotive with Cabry valve gear with cylinders 14"x22" built by Societé de Seraing and an exactly similar one having 'all the refinements known heretofore'. The latter locomotive was attributed to Poncelet, Cabry's assistant on the Western lines, whose engine had apparently already attracted attention on account of the economies it gave. Nevertheless Cabry's system gave 14% more power and 25% economy of fuel whilst the locomotive also maintained higher speeds than Poncelet's machine. Reference was also made to tests between an older engine with 14" cylinders built by Cockerill with Cabry's gear and one from the Seraing Works with 14" cylinders and variable exhaust. Again Cabry's system came out best by 20½% less fuel consumption and 5% greater speed. In another article,[22] Auguste Delaveleye described the Cabry valve gear and mentioned the bonus scheme for engine crews referred to earlier.

Another good critical appraisal of the gear was given by Felia Mathias, engineer and engine inspector at Orleans (and connected with Meyer, inventor of another variable expansion gear, at Mulhouse), generally confirming the shortcomings already mentioned.[23] Mathias also stated that the gear was operated by a threaded rod in a fixed sleeve. If this was so, this refinement pre-dated its supposed invention, by John Ramsbottom of the London & North Western Railway, by nearly twenty years.

The wider use of Cabry's valve gear

ON this side of the channel the *Railway Chronicle*, which first appeared in 1844, gave the Cabry gear quite a lot of attention, as would be expected from a journal partly owned by the 'Railway King' George Hudson. He was a champion of Henry's brother Thomas, on the York & North Midland Railway, and no doubt wished to give maximum publicity to any Cabry achievements. This journal[24] described the form of the gear which gave variable expansion in the forward direction only, and reported that 'we are indebted for it to Mr Cabrey of York, where we have seen it at work with perfect success.' Cabry confirmed that one or more engines on the Y&NMR were fitted with the gear, as we shall see later. The benefits of simplicity of adaptation and general economy, especially for varying loads and gradients, were put forward and the Cabry gear was compared directly with the Stephenson link motion: it was suggested that neither was the final answer but they represented the most recent developments in the search for the ideal mechanism.

A series of articles on valve gears[25] at the time also attributed the gear to 'Mr Cabrey of York', an error which has persisted in print until recent times. However, as it is plain that a modified form of the gear was in use in England, it may be that Thomas Cabry was responsible for introducing the modification, hence the confusion over authorship of the invention, which was never patented in the British Isles. Further evidence of confusion is found in a report in Herapath's *Railway Magazine*.[26] 'A locomotive on the plan of Mr Cabrey C.E. of the York & North Midland has been put on the Belgian Railway. It is named the 'Fox'. As no engine of this name existed in Belgium at the time it would seem that this was a garbled version of reports from that country that a locomotive with Henry Cabry's

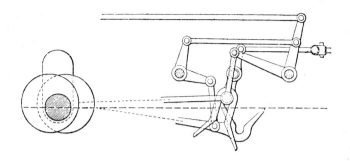

53. The British form of the Cabry valve gear

valve gear had been built by the Société du Renard of Brussels and which had lost something in translation.

Clark's *Railway Machinery* of 1855 described the Cabry gear and not only once again wrongly attributed it to Thomas Cabry of the 'North Midland Railway' [sic] but suggested that the lead increased as the valve travel was shortened whilst in fact the reverse was true. However FIG.53 taken from Clark, is shown as it is the simplest and clearest diagram of the British form of the gear to be found in contemporary sources.

A more recent description of the English version of the gear,[22] at any rate as it was applied to a batch of twelve locomotives supplied by Sharp Roberts & Co. to the South Eastern Railway in 1841/2, says that they had:

…an adaptation of the 'Cabry' gear with the fore-gear eccentrics between the wheels and the outer members of the inside frame and the back-gear eccentrics in the middle between the inner pair of inside frames. The fore-gear gabs engaged the upper arm and the back gear the lower arm of a rocking shaft. This 'Cabry' gear provided a modicum of expansive working by means of a very deep fore-gear gab in which the gab pin could be set at an intermediate (generally only one) position, thus producing a lesser valve movement. In the particular arrangement used by Sharps this special fore-gear gab was upon the rocking-shaft arm and the gab-pin on the end of the fore-gear eccentric rod whilst the back-gear gab was on the eccentric rod with the gab pin on the rocker arm. There were no dangerous oscillating levers on the footplate…

A version of Cabry's gear was used by several railways in what was until recently Czechoslovakia.

The railway companies there fitted a number of their locomotives with the gear when it was introduced and surprisingly new locomotives were apparently equipped with it until the end of the 1860s.[28]

Some further light is shed on contemporary views of the Cabry gear and the Stephenson link motion in a letter from Robert Thornton, locomotive engineer of the Edinburgh & Glasgow Railway, to the *Railway Chronicle*.[29] He drew attention to the fixed relation between the inlet and exhaust valves, being part of the same slide, and to the fact that the earlier in the stroke the steam was cut off the earlier the exhaust port opened, not allowing all the power to be extracted from the expanding steam before it was discharged. However, as this has been a feature of most valve gears ever since, it must be assumed that the more complicated mechanisms of expansion gears such as Meyer's (which had separate valves controlling the variable expansion) were not considered to give enough improvement in efficiency to justify their use.

A source of inspiration for the development of Walschaerts' valve gear

IT would seem highly likely that Henry Cabry's 'long gab' gear was one source of inspiration for his colleague Egide Walschaerts. As originally applied to the lower arm of the valve rocker, it provided a lever of variable throw whereby valve travel could be regulated. Its defect was the inability

THE WALSCHAERTS GEAR

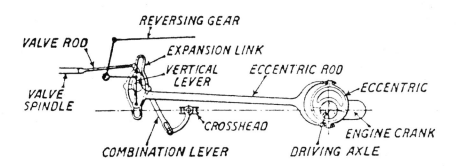

54 *(above).* **THE ORIGINAL WALSCHAERTS GEAR, 1844.**
As described in the text, this gear used a pivotted expansion link which was in effect two of Cabry's 'long gabs' facing inwards mounted on opposite ends of a rocking lever, the T-shaped eccentric rod having separate pins to engage each half of the link. Like Cabry gear, it was adjusted by raising or lowering the eccentric rod. The eccentric was at right angles to the crank and the secondary component of motion was derived from the crosshead through a combination lever pivotted to the expansion link. The secondary component was constant for all cut-offs.

55 *(below).* **THE IMPROVED WALSCHAERTS GEAR, 1848.**
While FIG 54 depicts a mechanism visibly descended from gab gear, this one embodies all the elements of a modern valve gear. Instead of varying the swing of the expansion link in the manner of Cabry gear, the link is now driven directly by the eccentric and oscillates through a constant angle. The top of the combination lever is driven by a radius rod attached to a die block sliding in the link, rendering the primary component of motion infinitely variable between full gear in either direction. As in its predecessor, the secondary component is generated from the crosshead and is constant at all cut-offs.

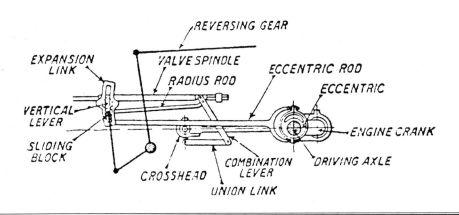

to alter valve travel selectively, that is to alter the primary component of motion while leaving the secondary unaltered. The solution was to generate the two components separately, to provide means for varying the primary, and then combine them. This is precisely what Walschaerts did.

The primary component of motion can be produced by an eccentric set ninety degrees ahead of the crank, which means that the fore and back eccentrics are diametrically opposite one another. A single eccentric arranged to drive either directly or through a first-order lever can therefore be substituted. The secondary component, being in phase with the crank, can be derived from the crosshead through a lever of suitable proportions. If the 'fixed pivot' of this lever be driven by the linkage producing the primary component of motion, both motions are combined to drive the valve, and this is exactly how the Walschaerts gear operates.

In his original gear of 1844, Walschaerts' single eccentric was provided with a T-headed rod carrying studs at each end of the crosspiece. This drove a lever which comprised two 'long gabs' facing inwards on opposite sides of the pivot and joined by curved extensions of the cheeks. If the eccentric rod was raised, the upper stud engaged the upper slot and drove the top arm of the lever in phase with the eccentric, its throw being determined by the position of the stud along the slot. If the rod was lowered, the bottom stud drove the bottom gab, so the top arm now moved in the opposite direction to the eccentric. From the top of the lever a rod ran back to a pivot near the top of a lever mounted on the end of the valve spindle, the lower end of this lever being driven by a horizontal link from the crosshead. The proportions of this *combination lever* were calculated to produce the correct secondary component of motion.

It is not known whether Walschaerts' 1844 gear got beyond the trial stage but in any case it contained the same weakness as Cabry's gear – it was adjusted by shifting the eccentric rod which thereby interfered with the effective angle of advance. As the object of separating the two components of motion was to eliminate the need for advancing the eccentric, this was rather self-defeating.

Four years later Walschaerts solved the problem by a simple rearrangement of the gear. Instead of varying the swing of the rocking lever, he made this into a curved, slotted link driven directly by the eccentric rod and driving the *radius rod* by means of a die block sliding in the link. The radius of the slot being equal to the length of the radius rod, primary valve travel was reduced by moving the die block nearer to the centre of the link and vice versa. Walschaerts must have been quite familiar with Cabry's gear: his crucial contribution, however, was the realisation that valve motion could be analysed in terms of two superimposed components bearing a fixed angular relationship to each other. By doing so he avoided the path of complication so fruitlessly travelled by John Gray[30] and others of his ilk and created the simplest and best of all reciprocating valve gears. The Walschaerts gear we know today is simply his 1848 gear turned round so that it fits between the crank axle and the cylinder, an obvious rearrangement first applied by Heusinger von Waldegg in 1862.

The development of the Stephenson link motion

THE continuous slotted link was first suggested by Williams in 1840 as a means of combining the travel of fore and back gear eccentrics into a single, continuously variable motion, but his notion of attaching the link directly to the eccentric sheaves was a mechanical impossibility. The idea was taken up by Howe in 1842 to produce the Williams-Howe link motion now known, quite incorrectly, as Stephenson valve gear.

As this valve gear rapidly replaced the gab motion for new locomotive construction it is worth briefly explaining why some locomotives were converted and other retained their original valve gear for many years. The reason is simply that in 1841 Robert Stephenson & Co. introduced a fundamental change in the design of inside cylinder engines by placing the valves between instead of on top of the cylinders, thereby creating the characteristic British locomotive of the Victorian era. Valves between the cylinders could be driven directly from the eccentrics without a rocking shaft and Stephensons were able to simplify the traditional gab gear by mounting a pair of gabs on the end of the valve spindle, one facing up and one down, suspending both eccentric rods from the same weighshaft and engaging the appropriate gab

THE DEVELOPMENT OF THE STEPHENSON LINK MOTION

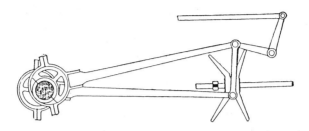

56. STEPHENSON GAB MOTION, 1841.
The direct ancestor of the Williams-Howe link motion was this simple
method of driving valves between the cylinders. There is a stud on the end
of each eccentric rod and both rods suspended are from a single weighshaft.
A year after Robert Stephenson & Co. introduced this gear, Sharp, Roberts
& Co. introduced their version in which both eccentric rods carried gabs
and one or the other was engaged with a stud on the valve spindle.

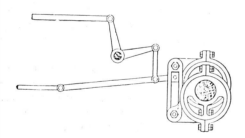

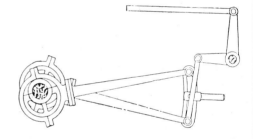

57. WILLIAMS LINK MOTION, 1842.
This was the first attempt to achieve variable
expansion by combining the motion of fore- and
back-gear eccentrics through the medium of a
slotted link, whereby the secondary component of
motion would remain constant – or nearly so – as
valve travel was reduced. Williams had got the right
idea but his method of achieving it by a straight link
attached directly to the eccentrics was geometrically
and mechanically imperfect.

58. HOWE-WILLIAMS LINK MOTION, 1843.
William Howe grasped the significance of Williams'
link and proposed this modification of Stephenson's
gab gear in which a curved link was attached to the
ends of the eccentric rods, its radius equal to the
length of the rods. The link enclosed a die block
pivoted to the end of the valve spindle. It was the
first and most widely applied of all link motions,
appearing only weeks before Daniel Gooch's 'fixed
link' motion. Williams and Howe were employees
of Robert Stephenson & Co., hence the gear
gradually became known as Stephenson gear and its
inventors largely forgotten; Robert Stephenson
himself always acknowledged its origin.

by raising or lowering the rods. This gear is correctly known as Stephenson gab motion and it will be apparent that by coupling the two eccentric rods by a link and replacing the gabs by a die block it could, at minimal cost, be converted into Williams-Howe link motion. Converting a locomotive with ordinary gab gear and valves on top of the cylinders required more fundamental alterations.

The change of cylinder position, together with developments in frame design, also affected the layout of Cabry's gear. In the original version of the gear, with variable expansion available in both directions, the four long forks were attached to the distribution shaft and engaged the studs on the end of each eccentric. The exact position of the eccentrics is not clear from the drawing which accompanied the patent specification but elsewhere the older arrangement with two eccentrics outside the cranks is shown.[31] It should be said that the foregoing applies to inside cylinder locomotives which were in the great majority at this period. When outside cylinders were employed each pair of eccentrics was placed just inside the frames next to the driving wheels. Locomotives with four eccentrics had first appeared in about 1835 and, due to the framing which was designed to offer maximum support for the cranks, two eccentrics were placed in the centre, between the cranks, and two outside. This was the arrangement adopted on the twelve SER locomotives already mentioned. As frame designs changed it became the practice to place all four eccentrics in the central position. As the valve motion was transmitted laterally by a rocking distribution shaft these arrangements made little difference to the gearing except that fewer parts were necessary.

There was also an intermediate form of Stephenson gab motion in which the ends of the eccentric rods were connected by a pot-bellied link that was, in effect, two Cabry long gabs joined together (the same shape as the rocking lever in Walschaerts' 1844 gear) that drove a stud on the end of the valve spindle. It had exactly the same characteristics as Cabry's gear with the added advantage of working equally well in reverse, but it is of rather academic interest because of the rapidity with which gab gear in all its forms was replaced by Williams-Howe and Gooch gear. It is pointless to speculate who was influenced by whom during this period, given the pace of locomotive development and the fact that the principal parties not only knew one another but were willing to discuss their difficulties.

It should also be emphasised that, up to 1843, nobody had produced a simple valve gear able to vary cut-off without significantly affecting lead, release and compression. Hawthorn and Gray had developed gears which went some way towards this ideal but they were mechanically unreliable, hence the contemporary interest in expansion valves. The picture changed completely once link motion became available and it was discovered that, unlike a stationary engine running at constant speed, a railway locomotive ran better at high speed if release and compression took place rather earlier. Link motion driving a simple slide valve was also much simpler than any expansion valve system.

General application of Cabry's valve gear

HENRY Cabry's long gab was a significant step along the path that led to the Walschaerts gear, being an early attempt to vary valve travel by imposing a variable-ratio lever between eccentric and valve spindle. It was simple to adapt from the traditional gab gear and there may have been resistance to more radical new ideas by locomotive manufacturers and the railway companies they supplied. This would have particularly applied to Sharps who were mass producers of standard models (although they did fit Bodmer's and Meyer's gear to special order, as was the case with the Cabry gear). Sharps did of course have a gear of their own – the Sharp & Roberts of *c.*1840 – a rather more complicated version of the gab gear aimed at simplicity of operation and not offering variable expansion. How Sharps came to adopt Henry Cabry's gear is not clear as the only locomotive built by them for the Belgian Railways during this period was the *Atlas* of 1839. This was two years before Cabry took out his patent, and, as no Sharp engines were supplied to the Y&NMR it is unlikely that Henry's brother Thomas was able to exert much influence with the builders. We can only assume that either Henry canvassed English builders or that one of the foreign orders specifying

WORKS NUMBER	DATE DELIVERED	RAILWAY	TYPE	DRIVING WHEELS	CYLINDERS	RUNNING NUMBER	NAME
160*	12.1841	SER	2-2-2	5′6″	13″ x 18″	1	Hengist
161*	12.1841	SER	2-2-2	5′6″	13″ x 18″	2	Horsa
173*	1.1842	SER	2-2-2	5′6″	13″ x 18″	3	Caesar
174*	2.1842	SER	2-2-2	5′6″	13″ x 18″	4	Vortigern
175*	2.1842	SER	2-2-2	5′6″	13″ x 18″	5	Vortimer
176*	2.1842	SER	2-2-2	5′6″	13″ x 18″	6	Ethelbert
177*	2.1842	SER	2-2-2	5′6″	14″ x 18″	7	Egbert
178*	3.1842	SER	2-2-2	5′6″	14″ x 18″	8	Sweyn
181*	4.1842	SER	2-2-2	5′6″	14″ x 18″	9	Canute
192	3.11.1842	M&HR	2-2-2	5′6″	13″ x 18″		Atalante
194	3.11.1842	M&HR	2-2-2	5′6″	13″ x 18″		Ulysses
196*	5.1842	SER	2-2-2	5′6″	13″ x 18″	10	Hardicanute
201*	7.1842	SER	2-2-2	5′6″	13″ x 18″	11	Ironside
202*	8.1842	SER	2-2-2	5′6″	14″ x 18″	12	Harold
236	11.1.1843	B&CR	2-2-2	5′0″	12″ x 18″†	1	
238	11.1.1843	B&CR	2-2-2	5′0″	12″ x 18″†	2	
240	11.1.1843	B&CR	2-2-2	5′0″	12″ x 18″†	3	
241	11.1.1843	B&CR	2-2-2	5′0″	12″ x 18″†	4	
299	1844	B&SR	0-4-2‡	4′6″	14″ x 20″†		Mars
300	1845	B&SR	0-4-2‡	4′6″	14″ x 20″†		Medea
322	12.1845	SA&MR	2-2-2	5′0″	15″ x 20″	17	Saturn
323	12.1845	SA&MR	2-2-2	5′0″	15″ x 20″	18	Bacchus
324	12.1845	SA&MR	2-2-2	5′0″	15″ x 20″	19	Cerberus
325	12.1845	SA&MR	2-2-2	5′0″	15″ x 20″	20	Alecto
326	12.1845	SA&MR	2-2-2	5′0″	15″ x 20″	21	Argus
327	12.1845	SA&MR	2-2-2	5′0″	15″ x 20″	22	Harpy(ie)

* All rebuilt between 1847 and 1855[37] when, no doubt, the Cabry gear would have been replaced.

† Outside cylinders.

‡ Although listed in Sharp's order books as 0-4-2s, these engines were in fact delivered as 2-4-0s.

TABLE 1. Locomotives built with Cabry's valve gear by Sharp Roberts & Co. at the Atlas Works in Manchester and delivered between December 1841 and December 1845.

the use of his gear brought it to Sharp's notice. It is somewhat surprising that it was still being requested on locomotives supplied to the Sheffield, Ashton & Manchester Railway as late as 1845 and even more so to find it in use in Central Europe until at least 20 years later.

It has not been possible to discover how long Henry Cabry's valve gear remained in use. In Belgium it may have lingered on for some time, in view of the completely different layout of Walschaerts gear and the consequent expense or impracticability of conversion of older inside-cylinder locomotives, although Stephenson's link motion may also have been used at first. In Central Europe it must have lasted into the 1870s. However in England conversion to Stephenson's link motion would have been a relatively simple matter and some light is thrown on this subject by Henry's brother, Thomas, when he was giving evidence in connection with the law-suit brought by John Gray against the L&NWR.[32] Thomas Cabry was rather vague but did say that his brother's gear had been abandoned some time before 1851, being superseded by the link motion, and he also confirmed that he had tried it on the Y&NMR. Valuable information about the length of time the Cabry gear remained in use in England could have been obtained from the locomotive registers for the SA&MR engines at Gorton works and similar records for SER engines at Ashford which were still available for research in the early 1960s.[33] Unfortunately both these sets of records seem to have been destroyed subsequently.[34]

It is, however, interesting to find a reference to Cabry's gear in John Bourne's *Catechism of the Steam Engine* published as late as 1872. Whilst he mentions other gears he only gives a detailed description of the Stephenson and Cabry devices at a time when Cabry's gear must surely have long fallen out of general use.

Details of locomotives fitted with the gear

THE order books of Sharp Roberts & Co. (renamed Sharp Bros in 1843),[35] of the Atlas Works at Manchester, identify twenty six of their engines (twenty four 2-2-2s and two 2-4-0s) as being built with Henry Cabry's valve gear. They were delivered between December 1841 and December 1845, twelve to the South Eastern Railway,[36] six to the Sheffield, Ashton & Manchester Railway. The remainder were supplied to three German companies, the Magdeberg & Halberstadt, the Bohn & Cologne and the Berlin & Stettin Railways. Details are given in TABLE 1. The order from the M&HR is annotated 'Cabry's expansion gear to be applied, and a charge to be made – one modification of Cabry's plan'. That from the B&CR is annotated 'If Cabry's plan of expansion be ordered within 6 weeks to be applied and to be charged £20 per engine': and the 'expansion slide valve to be arranged to work expansively during 3/10ths of the stroke. The forward and backward eccentric forks to work the weigh bars from the top and bottom'.

A report in the *Railway Chronicle* of 4 January 1845 lists 29 locomotives of the Belgian State Railways that had been fitted, or were about to be fitted (†), with Cabry's valve gear. These are listed in TABLE 2. As all but one were built before the date of Cabry's patent (31 July 1841), it is likely that their valve gear was modified subsequently. These locomotives were allocated to the Brussels–Mechlin–Liège line where the terrain is much more hilly than in west Belgium. Being fitted with variable expansion gear they were no doubt deployed where they could be used to the best advantage.

The 2-4-0 engines shown in TABLE 3 and built for the Belgian State Railways by Société St Leonard of Liège, are believed to have been fitted with the Cabry valve gear.[38] Later members of the class, which were not built until 1848, were less likely to have been so fitted.

The delivery of a pair of 2-2-2 engines built by the Société du Renard of Brussels (Works nos 18 & 19) for the Holland Railway was delayed until November 1842 and January 1843, owing to the last minute decision to fit them with the Cabry gear.[39] They had 1655mm driving wheels and 356x452mm cylinders, and were used on the Amsterdam to Leiden line. They were numbered 9 and 10 and carried the names *Orion* and *Sirius*.

These lists do not claim to be comprehensive, as it seems likely that further locomotives were fitted with Cabry's gear, particularly on railways in the German States.

NUMBER	NAME	MAKER	WORKS NUMBER	DRIVING WHEELS	CYLINDER DIAMETER	ENTERED SERVICE
0-4-2						
2	L'Elephant	R. Stephenson	100	4′6″	14″	1.5.1835
2-2-2						
6	Le Belge	Cockerill	1	5′0″	12½″	30.12.1835
8	L'Hercule	R. Stephenson	122	4′6″	14″	15.5.1836
12	Le Progrès	R. Stephenson	136	5′0″	12″	7.12.1836
20	Charles Quint	Cockerill	13	5′0″	12″	9.9.1837
22	Les Quatre Journées	Cockerill	14	5′0″	12″	22.9.1837
25	Robert Fulton	Cockerill	16	5′0″	12″	27.11.1837
26	St Hubert	R. Stephenson	172	5′0″	12½″	20.12.1837
28	Oudegherst	Cockerill	12	5′0″	12″	7.4.1838
36	Delvaux	R. Stephenson	168	4′6″	14″	3.6.1838
38	Pêpin de Landen	Cockerill	20	5′0″	12″	26.5.1838
42	Despautère	Cockerill	24	5′0″	12″	24.7.1838
44	Le Tonnerre	R. Stephenson	217	5′0″	14″	3.8.1838
64	La Constitution	Cockerill	30	4′6″	14″	22.3.1839
65	Teniers	Cockerill	32	4′6″	14″	3.4.1839
67	Quentin Metsys	Cockerill	33	4′6″	14″	27.4.1839
68	Notger	R. Stephenson	242	5′6″	12½″	7.5.1839
71	Le Sanglier des Ardennes	Cockerill	47	5′0″	12″	3.6.1839
82	Brederode	Cockerill	63	5′0″	12½″	27.9.1839
88	Lairesse	Cockerill	54	5′6″	12½″	8.1.1840
99	Helena †	R. Stephenson	296	5′6″	12½″	25.2.1840
107	Gramaye	Longridge	126	5′6″	12¾″	19.5.1840
108	Philippe le Bon	Longridge	127	5′6″	12½″	19.5.1840
110	Rega	Soc. de Renard	9	5′6″	12½″	6.6.1840
112	Verheyen	Longridge	133	5′6″	12″	6.8.1840
123	Butkens	Cockerill	80	5′6″	12½″	17.2.1841
124	Laruelle	Soc. de Renard	10	5′6″	12½″	19.3.1841
125	Sanderus	Soc. St Leonard	4	5′0″	12″	18.6.1841
137	Pierre David	Soc. St Leonard	14	5′6″	13″	5.7.1843

TABLE 2. 29 locomotives on the Belgian State Railways
which were fitted with Cabry's valve gear.

NUMBER	NAME	WORKS NUMBER	DRIVING WHEELS	CYLINDERS	ENTERED SERVICE
145		18	6′6″	15″ x 22″	12.1844
149	Le Général Evers	19	6′6″	15″ x 22″	3.1845
150		21	6′6″	15″ x 22″	3.1845
151		20	6′6″	15″ x 22″	3.1845

TABLE 3. 2-4-0 locomotives built for the Belgian State Railways by Société St Leonard and believed to have been fitted with the Cabry valve gear.

The Brake Carriage

THE invention of the sledge or slide brake has been attributed to Timothy Hackworth,[40] but some doubt exists as no evidence has been found and he did not patent the device. On the Continent nine locomotives, fitted with sledge brakes behind the driving wheels, were built by M. Postula of the Ateliers du Renard in Brussels for the opening of the Antwerp–Ghent Railway in 1842.[41] One of these engines was preserved and was sent to England in 1925 for the Stockton & Darlington Railway centenary celebrations and can still be seen in the railway museum at Brussels Nord station. We cannot be sure whether Henry Cabry got the idea for his brake carriage from these early Belgian engines but it seems quite likely.

On the line from Mechlin to Liège, an abrupt change of level existed near Liège. Two inclined planes were constructed between Ans and Liège at gradients of 1 in 34½ and 1 in 36, with a short level section half-way down, on which two stationary engines were placed to work the inclines by cable haulage. These inclines were operated in a rather more complicated way than at Goathland in Yorkshire and used a system of flags, bells and a trumpet. To control descending trains, Henry Cabry designed a six-wheeled 'break' carriage with four sledge brakes, two on each side between the wheels. The brake carriage weighed 8,000 kilogrammes (7 tons 2 cwt) and was approximately 20 feet long. FIG.59 shows a side view of the carriage and also details of the operation of the clutch mechanism for grasping the rope when ascending.

The sledges, shod with iron and mounted between the wheels, were applied by two brake-screws through levers and push rods. As the brakes were applied, an increasing proportion of the vehicle's weight was transferred to the sledges, increasing the retarding force until the whole weight was on the sledges. Further application lifted the wheels clear of the rails, depriving the carriage of guidance from the wheel flanges and exposing the sledge mechanism to lateral forces it was ill-suited to absorb. This was a draw-back of all sledge brakes, which had in any case to be raised clear of the track to negotiate pointwork safely. Cabry was not alone in his experiment with sledge brakes, but they never came into general use.

The efficiency of friction brakes is not constant – it diminishes with increased speed and as the surface of the fixed member (in this case the sledge) becomes heated and polished. This 'brake fade' was not recognised in Cabry's time and was first demonstrated in the historic brake trials carried out by William Stroudley and Captain Douglas Galton in 1878/9. It is probable that brakesmen were tempted to descend faster than they should and to wind the sledges down too far, sometimes running out of brakes towards the bottom of an incline. They would then screw the brakes down even harder in the mistaken belief that this would increase the braking effort. No doubt this is how the fatal accident involving Thomas Cabry's nearly-identical brake carriage on the Goathland incline occurred, the train being unable to stop before it met a set of points which caused the sledge mechanism to collapse.

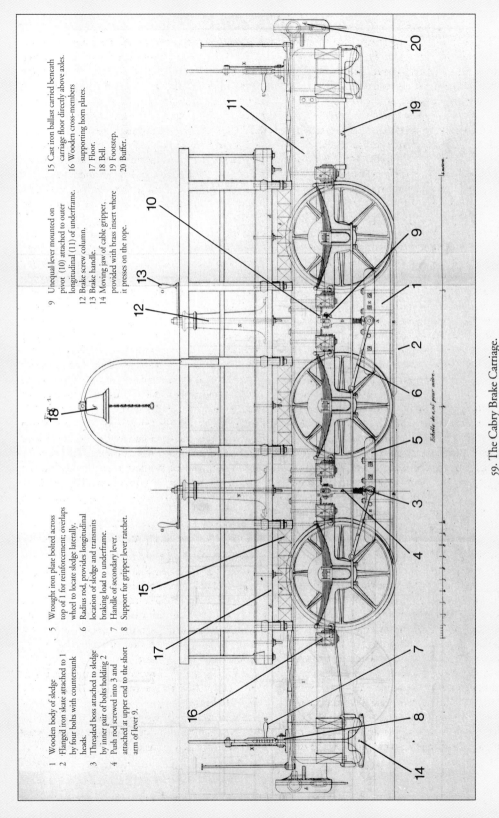

1   Wooden body of sledge
2   Flanged iron skate attached to 1
    by four bolts with countersunk
    heads.
3   Threaded boss attached to sledge
    by inner pair of bolts holding 2
4   Push rod screwed into 3 and
    attached at upper end to the short
    arm of lever 9.

5   Wrought iron plate bolted across
    top of 1 for reinforcement; overlaps
    wheel to locate sledge laterally.
6   Radius rod, provides longitudinal
    location of sledge and transmits
    braking load to underframe.
7   Handle of secondary lever.
8   Support for gripper lever ratchet.

9   Unequal lever mounted on
    pivot (10) attached to outer
    longitudinal (11) of underframe.
12 Brake screw column.
13 Brake handle.
14 Moving jaw of cable gripper,
    provided with brass insert where
    it presses on the rope.

15 Cast iron ballast carried beneath
    carriage floor directly above axles.
16 Wooden cross-members
    supporting horn plates.
17 Floor.
18 Bell.
19 Footstep.
20 Buffer.

59. The Cabry Brake Carriage.
For clarity, the key numbers only appear once. However, the parts referred to are in some cases duplicated on the brake carriage.
(Based on A. Delaveleye, Locomotives: Notice, 1842 and S.C. Brees, *Railway Practice – 4th series*. 1847.)

The Belgian brake carriages were used singly or in pairs according to the load. They preceded the train and when ascending were attached to the incline rope by means of a special clutch which was released when the train reached the top.

The clutch, or gripper, of which there was one at each end of the carriage, consisted of a fixed jaw mounted on the underframe and a moving jaw carried on the end of a long lever suspended from the operating linkage on the platform above. The rope ran along the centre of the track just below axle height, a few inches below the fixed jaw. To pick up the rope, the gripper arm carrying the moving jaw, normally held to one side at an angle so that it was well clear of the rope, was swung down to the vertical, closely fitting the arched sides of the main casting to minimise lateral strain on the gripper arm. It was then pulled straight up to lift the rope into the fixed jaw. The moving jaw was then tightened against the fixed one to grip the rope firmly. There would inevitably be some slippage during the time taken to grip the rope properly, for which reason the jaws were provided with brass inserts. These were tapered at their outer ends to allow the rope to flex freely right up to the moment it was finally gripped by the mechanism described below. These inserts presented a smooth and relatively soft surface to the rope, minimising wear and the danger of damaging the outside of the rope during engagement. To release the rope, the fixed jaw was dropped and swung to its resting position.

The operating mechanism (see FIGS 60–64) may at first sight seem rather complicated but was actually quite ingenious. As the bottom jaw had to be raised several inches in order first to collect the rope and then to lift it into the fixed jaw, only a small additional clamping movement was necessary to grip it. This called for a two-speed mechanism, fast when raising the jaw to collect the rope, slow when applying clamping pressure to grip it. Cabry's solution was to employ compound leverage. The larger, primary lever carried the gripper arm and could be secured by a latch at its outer (handle) end. Lifting this lever as far as it would go captured the rope, which would then be slipping through the closed gripper jaws. Pivotted to the primary lever near its outer end and lying along it with a handle near the gripper arm pivot was the secondary lever, the outer end of which carried two teeth to engage with rounded teeth on the inside curve of the quadrant for the primary lever. When pulled upwards, it acted like a crowbar and lifted the primary lever sufficiently to engage the next tooth on its own quadrant. The greatly increased mechanical advantage of the compound lever achieved a higher clamping force with correspondingly reduced upward movement of the jaw.

The gripper lever was cranked, the part above its pivot being at an angle to the bottom end so that when pulled into a near-vertical position and secured (presumably by a chain) the bottom end carrying the moving jaw was angled to one side clear of the rope, as described earlier. The offset in the lever took its centre of gravity far enough beyond the pivot to ensure that when released it fell into the operating position with the jaw directly below the rope – for obvious reasons the rope could only be picked up when it was close to the centre-line, i.e. on straight or very gently curving track. To grip the rope, the conductor released the gripper lever and as soon as it swung over he reached down and pulled up the primary lever until it stopped. He then transferred his hand to the handle of the secondary lever and pulled this right up once or twice to tighten the grip on the rope, doing so fast enough to prevent excessive rope slip but not so violently as to grip instantaneously and shock-load both the rope and his train. To release the rope he simply dropped the primary lever, reached across and pulled the upper end of the gripper lever towards him, fastening it in a vertical position with its chain.

Cabry may have been the first to design a successful gripper mechanism for capturing and releasing a continuously-running rope: on the London & Blackwall Railway, opened in 1840, cable haulage was used for the first ten years but the cable was stopped while carriages were attached. As carriages were detached without the train stopping at intermediate stations, only a much simpler grip was required to release the moving rope. W. J. Curtis, a prolific inventor, designed a gripper for use on the L&BR.[42] However, the gripper actually used is attributed to one of the engineers of that line, G.P. Bidder.[43]

As stationary engines were in use on early railways in a number of places, various methods were contrived to attach trains to the rope. The London

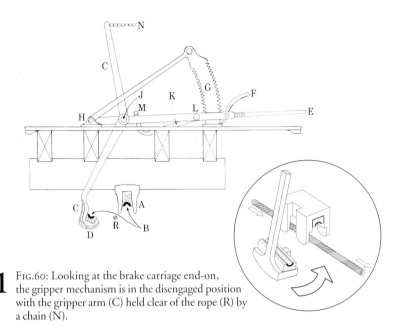

1 FIG.60: Looking at the brake carriage end-on, the gripper mechanism is in the disengaged position with the gripper arm (C) held clear of the rope (R) by a chain (N).

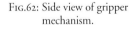

FIG.62: Side view of gripper mechanism.

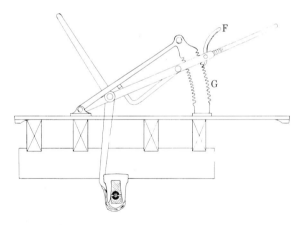

3 FIG.63: The operator raises the primary lever as much as he can and the jaws close but do not tighten enough to avoid slippage. The lever is held by the latch (F) which engages in the teeth on the outer edge of the quadrant (G).

The Cabry Brake Carriage gripper mechanism

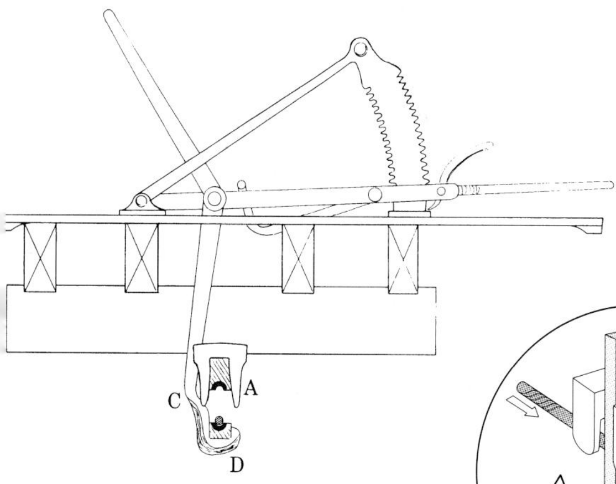

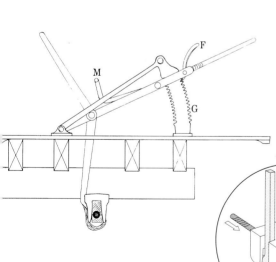

FIG.61: The gripper arm (C) has been released from the chain and has fallen under gravity gathering the rope and positioning it between the jaws A and D.

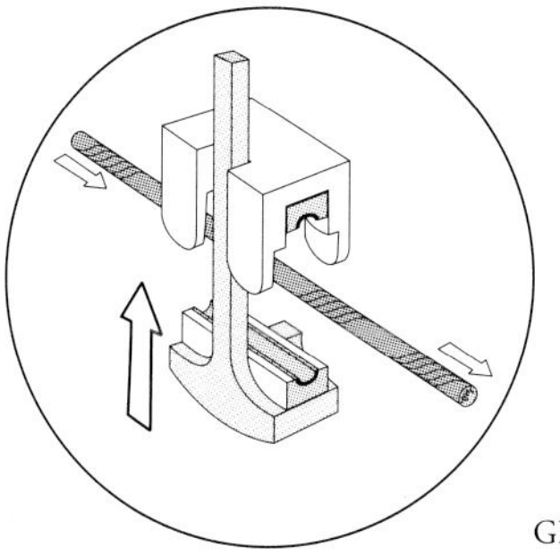

GRIPPER MECHANISM KEY

A Fixed jaw on underside of chassis
B Brass inserts in A and C to prevent frettage of the rope
C Gripper arm mounted onto primary lever E
D Moving jaw, brass lined, on end of C
E Primary lever
F Latch on E
G Quadrant
H Fixed fulcrum of E
J Moving fulcrum – C mounted on E
K Tightening or secondary lever
L Moving fulcrum – K mounted on E
M Handle on K
N Chain
R Rope

FIG.64: To squeeze the jaws tight, the operator grabs the handle M and raises the secondary lever which engages with the rounded 'teeth' on the inner edge of the quadrant (G) thus causing the primary lever latch (F) to move up another notch or two. The rope is now firmly held.

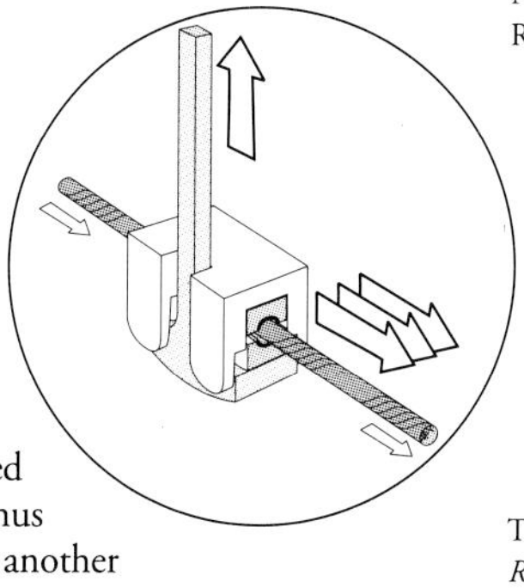

These drawings are based on S.C. Brees, *Railway Practice – 4th series.* 1847.

& Birmingham Railway's extension to Euston employed rope haulage from 1837 to 1844, and the Liverpool & Manchester Railway had rope-worked inclines from Edge Hill into the centre of Liverpool. In each case the rope was stopped to attach and detach trains, a smaller 'messenger' rope being used to attach trains to the main rope.

Gripper mechanisms for continuously-running ropes were used extensively on cable tramways later in the 19th century, with the rope running in a conduit below rail level on pulleys. A British engineer, Andrew S. Hallidie, emigrated to America in 1852. He established a wire rope manufacturing business in San Francisco and was responsible for the first cable tramway, opened there in 1873.[44] Quite soon, a number of such systems appeared in this country. The first was a short line up Highgate Hill, but in 1888 the first part of a more complicated system opened in Edinburgh. Here the gripper mechanism consisted of four small pulleys which supported the rope, with a pair of horizontal jaws to grip the rope firmly.[45] A similar method was used in Birmingham several years later[46] and these grippers were considered to be a refinement of the American grip which gathered the rope from above in a V-shaped 'crotch'. Nevertheless, this simpler device has outlived its British successors and is still in use in San Francisco to this day (1994). To what extent Hallidie was influenced by Henry Cabry's earlier efforts we shall probably never know.

Another British application of cable haulage was the Glasgow District Subway. This 4ft-gauge line opened in 1897 and each train had a gripper which supported the rope on a jaw with a renewable die of rolled steel. The top jaw, similarly lined, was brought down to grip the rope by a system of links and levers, wheel-operated by the driver.[47] The line was electrified in 1935.

When descending, Cabry's brake carriages were sometimes preceded by a sledge which slid on the rails by means of two iron patins, giving yet more braking power.[48] It was claimed that, if the rope broke, the brake carriages were able to bring the train to a halt almost immediately,[49] but it was nevertheless deemed prudent to provide an escape turn-out on each track at the foot of the incline.[50]

The Cabry brake carriage was also used on the Aix-La-Chapelle incline between Liège and Cologne. This incline was 1⅓ miles long on a gradient of 1 in 38 – similar in length and steepness to the Liège inclines. It is perhaps surprising that locomotives were not used on these inclines from the outset, as the Lickey Incline in England was two miles long with a gradient of 1 in 37 using locomotive power, and some early railways which used stationary engines at first gave them up at about the time the Belgian ones were introduced.

At a meeting at the Institution of Mechanical Engineers in 1851, some years before the abolition of cable working at Liège, a paper was read by Captain Laws describing the working of an incline of 1 in 27½ at Oldham on the Lancashire & Yorkshire Railway.[51] During the ensuing discussion it was asked why the Liège incline was not 'worked in a better manner' as apparently frequent division of trains caused delays to all eastbound traffic. Robert Stephenson said he had been consulted by the Belgian authorities but he could not oblige them to take his advice. He therefore assumed a 'greater timidity and want of confidence in the power of the breaks and of mechanical contrivances than was felt in England'.

Cable working on the Ans–Liège section was superseded in September 1871, locomotive haulage having been used for passenger trains since 1866. Heavy-duty locomotives were introduced to replace stationary engines which were proving increasingly unequal to the heavier freight traffic on the line.[52]

The Steam Trumpet

DURING the period when Henry Cabry was in charge of the locomotives on the Leicester & Swannington Railway his name became associated with the invention of a steam trumpet. Apparently this was prompted by a collision between the locomotive *Samson* and a farm cart on a level crossing near Thornton, on the L&SR, on 4 May 1833.[53] The event was first reported in a history of the Midland Railway published in 1876[54] and was then taken up by the well-known railway historian Clement Stretton. He was a prolific writer on railway subjects and, as a resident of Leicester, took a great interest in the history of the L&SR. He frequently promulgated the story of the steam trumpet and claimed that as a young man he had access to plans and documents stored at the company's station at Leicester West Bridge.[55] Before the offices were cleared out in 1869, at which time many documents

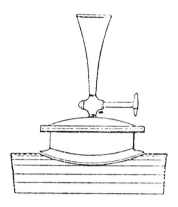

[Copy.]

LEICESTER AND SWANNINGTON RAILWAY.

Steam Trumpet.   Height, 1 ft. 6 in.; diam. of top, 6 in.

Engine Superintendent's Office, Leicester.
(Signed) HENRY CABRY.
May, 1833.

60 *(left)*. The steam trumpet for use on the Leicester & Swannington Railway, the design of which was attributed to Henry Cabry.

61 *(below)*. The locomotive *Hercules* belonging to that company was one of several fitted with the steam trumpet, according to the Leicester railway historian Clement Stretton. *Based on the C. Stretton blue prints, Leicester Museum of Technology.*

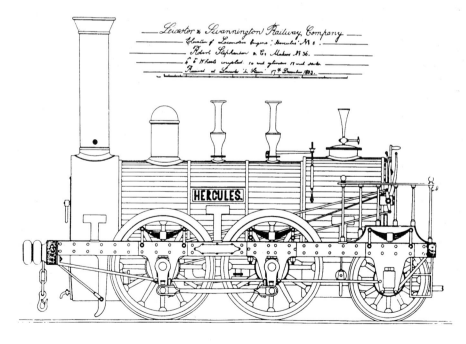

were destroyed, Stretton was given permission to take copies of some of the plans and drawings, making blue prints which are now at the Museum of Technology in Leicester. One of these blue prints depicts the steam trumpet and was apparently signed by Henry Cabry, although the reproduced signature is written by Stretton, or whoever drew the copies for him, and is quite unlike Cabry's actual signature. The writing on these blue prints closely resembles that on other copies sent to the London & North Western Railway by Stretton depicting early Liverpool & Manchester Railway locomotives.[56] As the blue print of the steam trumpet[57] is the only direct evidence of its existence it is unfortunate that it is only a copy, especially as much of Stretton's work has come to be regarded with extreme caution by historians.[58]

Whether the steam trumpet was ever fitted to a locomotive remains an intriguing mystery and it is of passing interest that the famous English organ builder William Hill was also experimenting with a steam trumpet shortly afterwards. In November 1838 he wrote to a Mr Birkett of Newcastle concerning the recent death of Birkett's brother, with whom he had been corresponding about the device.[59] Hill does not appear to have proceeded with his idea but it is surely no coincidence that a steam organ of eight pipes, mounted on the front of the locomotive *Tyne* during the opening celebrations of the Newcastle & Carlisle Railway in 1838, was the invention of the Reverend James Birkett, Vicar of Ovingham, near Newcastle,[60] moreover, his death was reported later in the same year.[61]

Two other references can be taken as tending to support the existence of some type of kindred device. The first comes in the form of a favourite after-dinner story often told by John Camidge, organist of Beverley Minster from 1875 to 1933, and suggests that George Hudson had some reeds on steam pressure fitted to locomotives on the York & North Midland Railway at York to warn of the impending departure of trains. The story has it that this prompted Camidge's grandfather, then organist of York Minster, to have powerful reeds fitted to the Minster organ, the work being done by the organ builder William Hill. This narrative is supported by an entry in a notebook of a local York historian, J. W. Knowles, written in 1924 telling a very similar story.[62]

Henry Cabry's later years

ALTHOUGH Henry Cabry lived in Belgium for the rest of his life, he evidently made a number of visits to England in the early 1840s. In a letter to Daniel Gooch, the Great Western Railway locomotive superintendent,[63] he referred to a recent visit to London and Summerside says:

I remember to have seen him after his return home, with Mr Stephenson, at our works at Ambergate; and there we renewed our friendship, and enlivened our conversation with incidents which occurred in our early days; for it was upon the 'Bobby' incline that I rang the bell a short distance from where he worked, and occasionally interchanged with him.

Francis Whishaw[64] travelled widely studying the early railway companies. In 1844 he toured the Belgian railways and met Henry Cabry on several occasions. Cabry provided him with details of Belgian permanent way and it was apparently the practice at that time to char the wooden sleepers rather than use a preservative. He also learned that it was usual to secure the rails with iron keys. However Cabry informed him that the English system of wooden keys was likely to be adopted.[65] Cabry also arranged for him to visit the famous ironworks at Seraing run by the Englishman, John Cockerill, and which built a number of early locomotives for the Belgian railways.[66]

George Bidder also received help from Henry Cabry when he passed through Belgium on his way to Switzerland in 1850 and wrote to his wife Georgey:[67]

I went this morning to inspect some very beautiful Stationary Engines on the model of what were once on the Blackwall Railway (London end) and at 11 am started by a special engine (which Mr T. Cabrey gave us) for Verviers…

Bidder is of course referring to the stationary engines then in operation at Liège but must surely have meant 'Mr H. Cabrey', unless Thomas Cabry paved the way for Bidder's visit by writing to Henry to make the necessary arrangements.

Henry became a naturalised Belgian citizen on 13 October 1846[68] and remained in the service of the Belgian State Railways, latterly becoming Inspector-General.[69] His wife died in 1868 at the age of 50 but Henry lived until his 76th year, dying in Brussels on 6 March 1881.

APPENDIX A
The Cabry family trees

Joseph Cabry = Mary Radclif
m. 9 Jan 1738/9
Hexham with Stonecroft RC

Joseph Cabry
c. 16 July 1739
Hexham with
Stonecroft

Thomas Cabry = Barbara Dawson
b. Hamsterley
m. 25 April 1770
Medomsley
bur. 18 Feb 1774
Tanfield

Barbara Cabry = John Nichols
m. 28 Feb 17
Tanfield

Thomas Cabry = Ann Mensforth
c. 7 March 1771
m. 18 Oct 1801
Monkwearmouth
d. 1838, Wirral

Joseph Cabry = Mary Wright
c. 21 June 1772   b. August 1769
Tanfield   Auckland St Helen
m. 16 June 1798   d. 23 Jan 1847
Gateshead St Mary   Wirral aged 78
d. 16 Sept 1858
York aged 86

Barbara Cabry
c. 24 March 1799
Ryton

Thomas Cabry = Margaret Ann
b. 6 June 1801   Bookless
New York   c. 11 May 1814
nr Newcastle   Acomb
m. 3 June 1841   d. 19 May 1887
Acomb   York aged 73
d. 5 Sept 1873
York aged 72

Joseph Cabry = Ann
b. 24 May 1803   b. c.1800
North Shields   Chester
m. c.1825   d. 7 Feb 187(
d. 26 Nov 1880   aged 75
Wirral aged 77

Joseph Cabry = Margaret Janet Day
b. c.1831   b. c.1835
m. 5 July 1855   d. 19 Aug 1912
Neston   Bournemouth
d. 22 Oct 1897   aged 77
Newcastle aged 66

Mary Jane Cabry = John Green
c. 29 Dec 1826   b. 1828
m. 27 May 1857   d. 18 Nov 1900
Wirral
d. 15 July 1901
Neston aged 74

Henry Cabry
b. c.1833
Neston
d. 8 Dec 1871
Ness aged 38

The Cabry Family
— ENGLISH BRANCH —

Mary Caberry = John Ramsey
c. 17 April 1774
Tanfield
m. 27 May 1798
Tanfield

Ann Cabry = John Hog
m. 2 July 1808

Henry Cabry = Elize-Mattilde
b. 5 June 1805   Vifquain
Percy Main   b. 21 Feb 1818
m. 14 Mar 1839   Brussels
Brussels   d. 15 April 1868
d. 6 May 1881   Brussels
Brussels

Jane Cabry = Thomas Pover
b. 7 May 1808   b. c.1807
m. 14 Dec 1842
Neston
d. 25 Jan 1877

Catherine Cabry = John Maylor
b. 8 July 1810
m. 26 Oct 1837
Neston

TO CHART 2

Charles Cabry = Jane Judson
b. c.1835   b. c.1839
m. 9 Oct 1880   d. 25 Sept 1909
d. 24 Jan 1900   Knaresborough
Knaresborough   aged 70
aged 64

Hannah Cabry = Thomas Mealor
b. 1839   b. c.1837
Ness   d. 3 April 1904
m. 1869   Raby aged 67
d. 8 March 1920
Wirral aged 80

Barbara Ann(e) = James (or Henry)
Cabry   Smith
b. 1837
m. 1862
Wirral

Thomas Cabry = Mary
b. c.1842   b. c.1847
Ness   d. 23 (or 29) Oct
m. 1869   1894
Gt Boughton   Neston aged 47
d. 13 Nov 1882
Birkenhead aged 40

Jean-Bruno Bourla = Louise Bal
b. ? Tournai   d. 1 Sept 1824
d. 13 March 1813, Paris   Paris

(Two other children)

Aglaé Bourla = Alexandre Vifquain
b. 21 Aug 1797   b. 22 June 1800
Paris   Tournai
m. 25 April 1827   d. 22 April 1859
d. 9 Dec 1840   Brussels
Brussels

Antonia-Zoé Georges = Pierre Simons
b. 28 June 1807   b. 22 Jan 1797
Paris   Brussels
d. ? Liège   m. 24 June 182
d. 14 May 184
at sea

Virginie Vifquain = Pierre-Jean Missale
b. 5 Aug 1833   b. 18 March 1820, Breda
Brussels   d. 13 July 1891, Brussels

FROM CHART 1

Henry Cabry = Elize-Matthilde Vifquain
b. 5 June 1805, Percy Main   b. 21 Feb 1818, Brussels
m. 14 Mar 1839, Brussels   d. 15 April 1868, Brussels
d. 6 May 1881, Brussels

Marie-Louise (Fanny) Cabry = Leon Weber
b. 7 April 1840, Molenbeek St Jean   b. 28 Nov 1828, Louvain
m. 1 Oct 1861   d. 6 Sept 1899
d. 8 June 1873 (in childbirth   Brussels aged 70
– 2nd child also died) aged 33

Maurice Weber = Emilie Van Hoorde
b. 25 Aug 1866   b. 23 April 1863, Brussels
m. 26 Feb 1889   d. 8 March 1942
d. 28 April 1951   Mont Saint-Guilbert
aged 84   aged 78

Edouard Weber = Suzanne
b. 28 Jan 1900   b. 3 Jan 1890
d. 14 Jan 1920   d. 5 Nov 1944

France-Louise Bourla = (1) Louis-Denis Georges
b. 12 Dec 1781, Paris   d. 2 Aug 1813, Aix-La-Chapelle
m(1) unknown   = (2) Jean-Baptiste Vifquain
m(2) 29 Jan 1817, Tournai   b. 24 June 1789, Tournai
d. 26 Aug 1834, Brussels   d. 31 Aug 1854, Ivry-sur-Seine

(2) Second marriage

(1) First marriage

Armande Georges = Gustave de Ridder
b. 10 April 1809   b. 31 May 1795
Brussels
m. 25 April 1827
d. 27 May 1862
Mée (France)

Louise-Therese
Vifquain

The Cabry Family
— BELGIAN BRANCH —

Marcel Weber = Neley Behn
b. 23 Dec 1897   b. 3 Sept 1902
d. 25 Aug 1957   m. 30 May 1923

Marc Weber = Micheline de Thibault de Boesinsinghe
b. 19 June 1928   b. 5 March 1932
m. 9 June 1956

References

Recurring references:

Richard S. Lambert, *The Railway King, A Study of George Hudson and the business morals of his time.* George Allen & Unwin 1934

William Weaver Tomlinson, *The North Eastern Railway. Its Rise and Development.* Andrew Reid & Co, Newcastle 1914.

ICE – Institution of Civil Engineers

IME – Institution of Mechanical Engineers

PICE – Proceedings of the Institution of Civil Engineers

PIME – Proceedings of the Institution of Mechanical Engineers

PRO – Public Record Office, Kew

PRO RAIL 1066/1160

RCTS – Railway Correspondence and Travel Society

Introduction

1 Information supplied by Mr H. Murray of York. The date on the back of the photograph which is in the possession of the Weber family in Brussels and which was wrongly thought by them to be the date of Cabry's death – 25 April 1862 – could however be the date on which the photograph was taken. This may have been during his period of office as Sherriff of York.
2 Thomas Summerside, *Anecdotes, Reminiscences and Conversations of and with the late George Stephenson, Father of Railways.* Bemrose & Sons, London 1878.
3 Edmond Curtis. *The History of Ireland.* Methuen University Paperbacks.

Chapter One

1 Thomas Summerside, *Anecdotes, Reminiscences and Conversations of and with the late George Stephenson, Father of Railways.* Bemrose & Sons, London 1878 pp.15–16
2 The Earl of Strathmore, Sir Thomas Liddell and Stuart Wortley
3 L. T. C. Rolt, *George & Robert Stephenson – The Railway Revolution.* Longman 1960
4 Until the 1860s mines were ventilated using the upward draught of furnaces below ground
5 Letter, George Stephenson to Joseph Cabry, dated 21 December 1819 (IME Phillimore Collection)
6 Report of a lawsuit in the *Courant* April 1822.
7 Letter dated 2 March 1820 (IME Phillimore Collection)
8 Land Tax Returns 1829
9 W. Mortimer, *The History of the Hundred of Wirral.* 1847
10 The *Courant* April 1822

11 Land Tax Returns 1829
12 Letter, George Stephenson to Joseph Cabry, dated 30 June 1824 (IME Phillimore Collection)
13 W. O. Skeat, *George Stephenson – The Engineer and His Letters.* IME 1973 p.66
14 Thomas Longridge Gooch's articles of apprenticeship dated 6 October 1823 (IME Phillimore Collection)
15 The *Railway Times* 1839 p.442
16 Letter dated 8 May 1825 (IME Phillimore Collection)

Chapter Two

1 Ledger of Robert Stephenson & Co 1823–1831 (Science Museum, London)
2 Michael R. Bailey 'Robert Stephenson & Co 1823–1829'. *Newcomen Society –Transactions.* Volume 50 (1978–9) p.110
3 *PIME* 1874 Volume 25 p.16 Memoir to Thomas Cabry – These memoirs, although usually reliable as to events, are often less so for the sequence of such events – they can also be somewhat eulogistic
4 PRO RAIL 1066/1160 House of Lords Committee on the Great Western Railway Bill 1835. Also PRO RAIL 667/653 £3-5s paid to Thomas Cabry for work done on the Brusselton and Etherley engines
5 Bailey – Advice from George Stephenson to Robert Stephenson & Co dated 28 September 1824
6 Bailey, Appendix 1 – *See also* Bailey p.117 and T. L. Gooch diaries (ICE) for a typical cycle of events when installing a winding engine
7 T. L. Gooch articles op.cit.
8 T. L. Gooch Diaries (ICE)
9 Letter from George Stephenson to Joseph Cabry, dated Liverpool 30 June 1824 (IME Phillimore Collection)
10 Hebard's *Cyclopaedia* 1836 p.476
11 Robert Stephenson & Co ledger 1823–1831 at the Science Museum Library. Entry on 30 June 1826
12 Ibid. 30 September 1826 and 28 February 1827. See also Tomlinson p.158
13 R. H. G. Thomas *The Liverpool & Manchester Railway.* Batsford 1980 p.183
14 PRO RAIL 1066/1160. *See also* Bailey
15 Summerside op.cit.
16 Sidney Pollard *The Genesis of Modern Management.* Penguin Books 1965 p.96
17 Bailey, Appendix 5 – Pig Iron to the value of £180 supplied March 1828
18 Robert Stephenson & Co ledger 1823–31 at the Science Museum Library
19 Ibid. Entry on 31 August 1829
20 Ibid. Entry on 31 March 1830

21 Memoir of Thomas Cabry *PIME* 1874 p.16
22 Robert Stephenson & Co ledger 1823–31 at the Science Museum Library
23 C&WR board minutes (At the Cathedral Archives and Library, Canterbury)
24 Revd R. B. Fellows, *History of the Canterbury and Whitstable Railway.* J. A. Jennings, Canterbury 1930 p.39
25 C. R. Clinker. *The Leicester & Swannington Railway.* Avon-Anglia Publications 1977. p.49. In the meantime, from 9 July 1830 to April 1831, Richardson had held the position of assistant resident engineer to the Leicester & Swannington Railway, then under construction
26 C&WR board minutes
27 Ibid.
28 Fellows op.cit. p.41
29 The *Railway World* July 1969 p.318
30 PRO RAIL 1066/1160 p.96 and *see also* PRO RAIL 1149/9 I. K. Brunel Collection 'Facts' folios 158–161 – 'on level….engine came and pushed'
31 PRO MT 6/3/18 Correspondence and Papers – General Pasley's report to the Board of Trade 3 April 1846
32 C&WR board minutes 29 June 1832
33 Ibid. 6 August 1835
34 PRO RAIL 1066/1160 p.222 and PRO RAIL 1149/9
35 C&WR board minutes 15 February 1836
36 PRO MT 6/3/18
37 Fellows op.cit. p.55
38 C&WR board minutes 5 December 1831
39 Ibid. 6 February 1832
40 Ibid. 6 August 1835
41 Ibid. 3 July 1836
42 Ibid. 4 August 1836
43 Ibid. 12 February 1834
44 Ibid. 17 February 1834

Chapter Three

1 PRO RAIL 1008/114 Letters of T. L. Gooch to R. Gill (a Manchester & Leeds Railway director) dated 24 & 26 August 1836
2 PRO RAIL 343/2 M&LR board minutes, various dates between 1 August and 19 September 1836
3 PRO RAIL 770/1 Y&NMR board minutes
4 Ibid. 22 December 1836
5 Ibid. 29 December 1836
6 Ibid. – various dates
7 1 Vict.cap.XVIII. *See also* PRO RAIL 770/89 24 August 1837 – £126 paid for Thomas Cabry's expenses in London. PRO RAIL 770/13 (Y&NMR Prospectuses, Reports and Accounts 1836–1854) also contains a four page supplement to

notes & proceedings of the Y&NMR Amendment Bill of 1837, House of Commons Committee. On 21 April 1837 Thomas Cabry was examined in support of the bill

8 The *Railway Times* 6 February 1841 report of a discussion at the Y&NMR half-yearly meeting

9 PRO RAIL 770/1 14 March 1839

10 Ibid. various dates in 1838/9

11 Ibid. 20 June 1839

12 PRO RAIL 770/13 – Y&NMR half-yearly meeting 13 July 1838

13 See the *Railway Times* 1839 pp.442 & 779 for description

14 PRO RAIL 770/1 5 November 1840

15 Ibid. 26 November 1840

16 Lambert p.58

17 The *Railway Times* November 1840 p.989

18 *Royal Commission on Historical Monuments Volume III, City of York South West of the Ouse.* p.64

19 Information provided by the British Rail Property Board, York

20 PRO RAIL 527/8 North Eastern Railway board minutes 29 December 1854, Thomas Cabry appointed as engineer of the Southern Division, salary £700 pa. and 'house free as at present'

21 PRO RAIL 527/27 NER locomotive and way & works committee minutes 17 March 1865

22 Information supplied by Mr H. Murray

23 Information supplied by British Rail Property Board, York

24 PRO RAIL 530/3 North Midland Railway board minutes 16 November 1842

25 Ibid. 6 December 1842

26 Lambert p.76

27 PRO RAIL 530/3 14 January 1843

28 W. P. Marshall – later Secretary of the IME

29 PRO RAIL 530/3 6 December 1842

30 R. M. Robbins 'The North Midland Railway and it's enginemen 1842–3'. *Journal of Transport History* Volume 4 No.3 May 1960 pp.180–6

31 The *Railway Record* 28 July 1849 p.720

32 *Railway Locomotive Management, in a series of letters reprinted from the Railway Record.* Birmingham & London 1847

33 PRO RAIL 1053/1 – Letter R. Frost to The Board of Trade 10 February 1843

34 PRO RAIL 530/3 8 March 1843

35 Ibid. 4 April 1843

36 'Veritas Vincit' 21 February 1843

37 British Museum additional manuscripts 41989–41992

38 PRO RAIL 770/1

39 Ibid. 26 October 1837

40 Ibid. 28 December 1837

41 PRO RAIL 770/2 Y&NMR board minutes 28 January 1841

42 PRO RAIL 770/2 13 April 1843, 26 April 1843 & 8 September 1843

43 27 September 1845

44 PRO RAIL 527/35 NER locomotive and way & works committee minutes 11 August 1881 and 8 September 1881

45 Information regarding the subsequent history of the bridge (No.17) kindly supplied by the late Mr M. F. Barbey former district engineer, British Rail, York

46 7 November 1843

47 The *Railway Chronicle* 7 February 1846 p.123

48 PRO RAIL 386/7 London & Brighton Railway board minutes 14 September 1843

49 D. L. Bradley, *Locomotives of the London Brighton & South Coast Railway* Part 1, RCTS 1969 and PRO RAIL 386/7 L&BR board minutes, various dates

50 Editorial in the *Railway Times* 18 November 1843 p.1248

51 PRO RAIL 386/7

52 Ibid. 5 October 1843

53 Ibid. 13 October 1843

54 Ibid. 23 November 1843

55 Ibid. 23 November 1843

56 Bradley op.cit. Gray was appointed from 27 March 1845

57 The *Railway Times* 1843 2 December 1843 p.1295

58 PRO RAIL 386/21 L&BR traffic committee minutes 11 December 1843 'Mr Pountain(?) and Mr Chadwick' also 'Veritas Vincit' in the *Railway Times* 1844 p.81 'Cabry has taken a favourite Yorkshireman with him to be master over the shed'

59 The Brighton and South Eastern Railways at Redhill. The *Journal of the Railway & Canal Historical Society,* Volume II No.3 May 1956

60 The *Railway Times* 9 December 1843 p.1319

61 *R&CHS Journal,* Vol.II No.3 May 1956

62 The *Railway Times* 7 November 1843

63 'Veritas Vincit' 27 March 1844

64 PRO RAIL 770/2 – payment made on 15 December 1841

65 The *Railway Record* 11 February 1846 p.228 referring to 22 September 1845 & 17 January 1846

66 The *Railway Record* 11 February 1846

67 PRO RAIL 186/69 Eastern Counties Railway united extension committee minutes

68 PRO RAIL 186/38 ECR traffic committee minutes 28 October 1845

69 Ibid. 7 May 1846

70 The *Railway Record* 13 December 1845 pp.1919–21

71 The *Locomotive Magazine* 1939 p.206

72 The *Railway Record* 15 June 1848 p.588

Chapter Four

1 *Herapath's Railway Magazine* 1845 p.1123

2 Report in the *Railway Chronicle* 12 July

1845 p.832

3 PRO RAIL 1149/24 I. K. Brunel Collection – Board of Trade reports on railways 1843–5 – General Pasley's letter to the Board of Trade 30 August 1845

4 Manuscript at Science Museum Library of diary No.1 1825–1851 and extracts published in instalments in the *Railway Magazine* during 1908/9

5 Information from the research notes of E. Craven supplied by the late K. Hoole

6 Tomlinson p.484

7 PRO RAIL 1053/50 Correspondence between NER and BOT 1853–74, Captain Tyler's Report of the 29 August 1860 accident

8 PRO RAIL 770/82 Y&NMR journal (construction) 1846–1854

9 The *Yorkshire Gazette* 27 February 1864 – Report of the inquest on the incline accident

10 Ibid.

11 PRO RAIL 1053/50

12 A. J. Peacock & D. Joy, *George Hudson of York*. Dalesman Publishing Co 1971. *See also* A. J. Peacock, *George Hudson 1800 – 1871. The Railway King.* Published by the author, 1989 pp.276/278

13 *PIME* 1874 Volume 25 p.16

14 Lambert, Tomlinson and Peacock ibid. (reference 12 above)

15 PRO RAIL 770/12 York & North Midland Railway Committee of Inquiry 1849. Minutes of evidence

16 PRO RAIL 772/12 York, Newcastle & Berwick Railway Committee of Investigation 1849. Report and minutes. *See also* the research notes of E. Craven

17 *The Yorkshireman* 1 December 1849

18 H. S. B. Whitley 'Timber Viaducts in South Devon and Cornwall, GWR' The *Railway Engineer* October 1931 pp.384–392

19 PRO RAIL 770/13 Third Report of the Committee of Inquiry, Appendix A

20 Tomlinson p.649

21 Dr L. G. Booth 'Timber works' *The Works of Isambard Kingdom Brunel* edited by Alfred Pugsley. Cambridge University Press 1980

22 PRO RAIL 770/3 Y&NMR board minutes 3 August 1849

Chapter Five

1 Brian Lewis 'Brotherton Tubular Bridge: a surprising miscalculation?' *Journal of the Railway and Canal Historical Society* Volume XXVIII No.6 November 1985

2 PRO RAIL 770/35 Y&NMR reports and letters 1851–2. Letter dated 13 October 1852

3 PRO RAIL 1053/20 Railway Department report for 1852 pp.73–4 Captain Wynne's report of 19 November 1852

4 PRO RAIL 770/6 Y&NMR board minutes

5   The *Illustrated London News* 31 August 1850
6   Ibid. 12 October 1850
7   The *Yorkshire Gazette* 12 October 1850
8   Ibid. 4 September 1852
9   Ibid. 16 September 1854
10 Ibid. various dates between 1854 and 1858
11 Ibid. 12 February 1851
12 PRO RAIL 770/5 Y&NMR board minutes 12 February 1850 and PRO RAIL 1111/8 report and accounts Y&NMR and YN&BR 1848–54
13 PRO RAIL 770/14 Reports of Thomas Cabry 1850–1
14 Michael Robbins, From R. B. Dockray's diary. The *Journal of Transport History* Volume 7 No.1 May 1965.
15 PRO RAIL 770/5 Y&NMR board minutes 17 May 1850
16 PRO RAIL 527/14 NER board minutes 6 November 1874
17 PRO RAIL 527/30 NER locomotive and way & works committee minutes 24 January 1873
18 PRO RAIL 770/5 14 June 1850 tender of Jno Walker of York accepted at £3.14.0 per ton
19 PRO RAIL 770/14
20 PRO RAIL 770/5 23 April 1851 & 30 April 1851
21 PRO RAIL 770/2 Y&NMR board minutes 24 August 1842, 21 September 1842 & 28 September 1842
22 PRO RAIL 236/16 GNR board minutes 20 March 1851 and subsequently
23 PRO RAIL 236/239 GNR occasional committee minutes 18 March 1850 and PRO RAIL 236/16 GNR board minutes – letter from Wilson dated 13 May 1851
24 Ibid. 9 August 1850
25 Census records
26 Manuscript transcript presented to the IME by Edward Woods 1876
27 Patent No.7745 of 1838
28 R. T. Smith 'John Gray and his expansion valve gear' *Newcomen Society – Transactions.* Volume 50 (1978–9) p.145
29 Smith op.cit.
30 South Lancashire Assizes, Liverpool 27 August 1851 – Smith p.7
31 Superintendent of the Monkland & Kirkintilloch Railway
32 An inventor and Professor of Machinery at University College, London. He was later Superintendent of Specifications and Clerk to the Commissioners of Patents, thus appearing as an expert witness on patent infringements
33 Smith op.cit.& E. Craven research notes
34 PRO RAIL 313/2 H&HR provisional committee minutes 31 August 1852
35 Ibid. 19 August 1852
36 PRO RAIL 313/3 H&HR directors minutes 2 August 1853
37 PRO RAIL 313/1 H&HR shareholders minutes 30 July 1853

38 Ibid. 24 December 1853
39 PRO RAIL 313/3 various dates
40 Ibid. 18 April 1854
41 PRO RAIL 1111/14 H&HR half-yearly reports – 7 years from 1 January 1856
42 PRO RAIL 527/26 NER locomotive committee minutes 16 January 1863
43 PRO RAIL 770/5 1 October 1851
44 PRO RAIL 770/6 12 January 1853
45 Tomlinson p.520
46 PRO RAIL 770/6 14 October 1852 & 2 February 1853
47 Ibid. 21 July 1852

Chapter Six

1   Information from the research notes of E. Craven, supplied by the late K. Hoole
2   PRO RAIL 527/8 NER board minutes 29 December 1854
3   Ibid. 29 December 1854
4   Ibid. 17 November 1854
5   PRO RAIL 527/11 NER board minutes 27 November 1863 – Fletcher's salary increased to £1000 and Bourne's to £800 (in line with Cabry) both with effect from 1 July 1863
6   Tomlinson p.551
7   PRO RAIL 527/8 22 September 1854
8   PRO RAIL 527/24 NER locomotive and way & works committee minutes 11 September 1857 and PRO RAIL 527/448 NER estimates 1854–1860, 23 October 1857
9   PRO RAIL 527/24 18 June 1858
10 PRO RAIL 1053/57 – Captain Tyler's accident report dated 21 October 1861
11 PRO RAIL 1053/50 – Captain Tyler's accident report of August 1860
12 PRO RAIL 1053/57 21 October 1861
13 PRO RAIL 1053/57 23 February 1864
14 G. W. J. Potter, *A history of the Whitby & Pickering Railway.* The Locomotive Publishing Co Ltd London 1906
15 PRO RAIL 527/1152, extracts from newspaper reports
16 The *Leeds Mercury* 22 September 1860
17 The *Yorkshire Gazette* 12 November 1864
18 Ibid. 26 November 1864
19 Ibid. Obituary to Thomas Cabry 13 September 1873
20 Window No.4 destroyed April 1942
21 Information supplied by Mr M. Greaves the present proprietor of the property, now the Carlton House Hotel
22 L. T. C. Rolt, *Isambard Kingdom Brunel.* Longmans 1957. pp.78/9
23 L. G. Booth 'Timber Works', *The Works of Isambard Kingdom Brunel.* VI edited by Alfred Pugsley. Cambridge University Press 1980
24 This and all subsequent contemporary information on timber structures on the York–Scarborough line come from PRO RAIL 1149/24 Board of Trade reports on railways 1843–1845

25 Tomlinson pp.636/7 and PRO RAIL 527/1197 Maintenance of Permanent Way – Reports 1857–1864, T. Cabry's Report dated 1 March 1866
26 Information supplied by North Yorkshire County Council, County Surveyor's Department
27 Ibid.
28 PRO RAIL 527/36 NER locomotive and way & works committee minutes 5 October 1882
29 PRO RAIL 527/1350 Cost of construction of Ripon Viaduct and other works 1862–8
30 PRO RAIL 527/1196 Maintenance of Permanent Way – reports 1854–60
31 PRO RAIL 527/958 NER table of distances, Southern Division 1862 – timber structures still in existence at that date are noted
32 PRO RAIL 527/1196
33 PRO RAIL 527/958
34 PRO RAIL 527/958
35 PRO RAIL 527/958
36 PRO RAIL 527/961 Extracts from newspapers 1853–1880
37 PRO RAIL 527/25 NER locomotive and way & works committee minutes 15 April 1869
38 Replaced by an embankment 1863/4 (Tomlinson pp.636/7). See also PRO RAIL 527/1197 (Extraordinary Works 1857) – Knottingley Viaduct to be converted to an embankment. 1858 – New top framing and prepare for filling up estimated cost £6500 – one quarter to be done each year. (Extraordinary Works 1861) Completion of replacement of Knottingley Viaduct
39 PRO RAIL 527/27 NER locomotive and way & works committee minutes 22 December 1865 and PRO RAIL 529/2366 Plan of old and new Malton viaducts. This plan is marked 'cancelled 20/12/18' so it is possible this viaduct was further rebuilt at that time
40 PRO RAIL 527/1197
41 PRO RAIL 527/1197 (1863) Knaresborough Branch Skip Bridge, replacement of decaying timbers etc. also PRO RAIL 527/32 NER locomotive and way & works committee minutes 3 June 1875 – Contract for reconstruction of the Skip Bridge at Marston. This makes the Marston bridge possibly the last timber bridge on the Southern Division of the NER to be rebuilt
42 PRO RAIL 527/1350 (T. Cabry's Report dated 1 March 1866) – Two wooden bridges on Leeds Northern Railway near Ripon estimated cost of renewal £22,000. Also PRO RAIL 527/409 – reports of engineer to directors 1865–80 (13 January 1869) – replacement of larger Ripon viaduct completed without accident or interruption to traffic (cost £14,028)

43 See reference 14 and PRO RAIL 527/1350 letter of 29 April 1866 – 16 wrought-iron girders of 75 feet and 28 of 50 feet – also specification dated 13 January 1868

44 PRO RAIL 527/1196 (Extraordinary Works 1858) – Wharram Viaduct sank considerably and requires support (cost £186-9-11d). Also PRO RAIL 527/1197 (1861) – Filling up of the Wharram Viaduct and replacing four other wooden bridges. However later entries show – 1863 Filling up Wharram Viaduct and 1864 Wharram Viaduct postponed for another year. So it must be presumed it was in fact filled up shortly after 1864

45 PRO RAIL 527/1196

46 PRO RAIL 527/1197

47 PRO RAIL 527/958

48 PRO RAIL 527/1350 – letter dated 1 March 1866 – Five wooden bridges over the River Esk will have to be replaced.

49 The *Railway Chronicle* 12 June 1847 pp.567/8

50 British Rail bridge plans at York

51 Ibid

52 Ibid

53 PRO RAIL 527/24 NER locomotive and way & works committee minutes 14 August 1857

54 Ibid.11 September 1857

55 PRO RAIL 527/35 NER locomotive committee minutes 24 February 1881

56 British Rail bridge plans at York

57 PRO RAIL 527/1196

58 PRO RAIL 527/11 8 September 1865

59 Tomlinson p.253

60 *PIME* 1874 Volume 25 p.16

61 PRO RAIL 527/28 2 March 1866

62 PRO RAIL 527/1350 Cost of construction of Ripon Viaduct and other works 1862–1868. Entry 19 June 1866

63 Ibid

64 Ibid. 27 September 1867

65 PRO RAIL 527/1350 – 28 November 1862

66 PRO RAIL 527/8 31 December 1858

67 Jack Simmons *The Railways of Britain,* 2nd Edition. Macmillan 1968 pp.82/3

68 RAIL PRO 527/25 19 November 1858

69 PRO RAIL 527/25 1 April 1859

70 Patent No.3084 of 1 December 1865

71 Tomlinson p.648

72 Simmons op.cit.p.83

73 PRO RAIL 527/27 20 January 1865 and PRO RAIL 527/409 NER reports, engineer to directors 1865–80. Thomas Cabry – letter to T. E. Harrison 20 March 1867

74 PRO RAIL 527/409 Thomas Cabry report dated 24 October 1867

75 Ibid.

76 From Thomas Cabry's obituary in the *Yorkshire Gazette* 13 September 1873

77 PRO RAIL 527/13 NER board minutes 28 April 1871

78 Ibid. 4 February 1870

79 From Thomas Cabry's obituary in the *Yorkshire Gazette* 13 September 1873

80 Lambert p.299

Chapter Seven

1 Land Tax Returns for 1829

2 PRO RAIL 56/2 2 January 1862

3 Ibid. 21 September 1865

4 PRO RAIL 527/27 NER locomotive and way & works committee minutes 25 September 1863

5 PRO RAIL 527/25 NER locomotive and way & works committee minutes 3 February 1860

6 PRO RAIL 527/29 NER locomotive and way & works committee minutes 5 November 1869

7 PRO RAIL 527/14 NER board minutes 30 August 1872 – salary £600 from 1 July 1871

8 Ibid. 20 November 1874

9 York Street Directory, 1872

10 PRO RAIL 527/38 NER locomotive committee minutes 5 November 1885

11 *PIME* 1878

12 The *Yorkshire Gazette* 19 November 1853

13 R. T. Smith 'John Gray and his expansion valve gear' – *Newcomen Society – Transactions* Volume 50 (1978–9)

14 PRO RAIL 527/7 NER board minutes 9 September 1853 – 'about to leave the Company's service'

15 *PIME* 1878

16 This information and much of that in the following paragraphs supplied by Mr R. N. Clements

17 Adjourned special meeting on 9 November 1865 – reported in the *Railway Times* 11 November 1865

18 J. Tatlow, *50 years of Railway Life in England, Scotland and Ireland.* The Railway Gazette 1920

19 E. L. Ahrons. – *Locomotive and Train Working in the Latter Part of the Nineteenth Century.* Volume 6. W. Heffer & Sons Ltd Cambridge 1954

20 PRO RAIL 1053/57. Report dated 6 February 1861

21 Addresses from *PIME* for relevant years

22 PRO RAIL 56/3 B&TR minutes 19 October 1865

23 PRO RAIL 56/27 B&TR half-yearly locomotive and rolling stock details 1859–73

24 PRO RAIL 56/1 B&TR board minutes 3 April 1856

25 PRO RAIL 527/96 – NER Newcastle committee minutes – 24 September 1874 and PRO RAIL 527/2188 NER revenue accountant's memo. book 1870–9, year ending 5 April 1883 – J. Cabry passenger superintendent at Newcastle. Salary £450

26 PRO RAIL 56/4 B&TR board minutes

27 PRO RAIL 527/37 NER locomotive and way & works committee minutes

28 The *Engineer* 4 January 1889 p.8

29 R. Carpmael 'The manufacture and use of steel railway sleepers.' *PICE* 1931

30 PRO RAIL 527/33 NER locomotive and way & works committee minutes 12 September 1878

31 PRO RAIL 527/366 2 September 1886

32 Ibid. 18 October 1888

33 PRO RAIL 527/42 NER locomotive committee minutes 26 July 1894 and PRO RAIL 1057/3097 NER report on the life of rails and other permanent way materials, H. Copperthwaite, C. A. Harrison and W. J. Cudworth. p.21

34 PRO RAIL 527/17 NER board minutes 1 June 1888

35 PRO RAIL 527/18 NER board minutes 19 February 1892 – Mr Cabry having retired... but last reference to him was 30 April 1891 and first mention of his successor 4 June 1891 in PRO RAIL 527/369 NER way & works committee minutes

36 Obituary in *Transport* 29 October 1897 p.350

Chapter Eight

1 Henry Cabry – Naturalisations No.663 at Algemeen Rijkarschief, Brussels

2 W. O. Skeat, *George Stephenson – The Engineer & His Letters.* IME 1973 p.39

3 C. R. Clinker, *The Leicester & Swannington Railway.* Avon-Anglia Publications 1977. p.51

4 J. Goussens, *Egide Walschaerts 1820–1901.* de Mijlpaal Mechlin Belgium 1984 p.57

5 Michael R. Bailey 'Robert Stephenson & Co. 1823–1829'. *Newcomen Society – Transactions.* Volume 50 (1978–9) p.115

6 Clinker. Op.cit. p.30

7 Ibid. p.31

8 PRO RAIL 359/2 Leicester & Swannington Railway board minutes

9 C. E. Lee – the *Railway Magazine* June 1935 p.425

10 Algemeen Rijkarschief, Brussels

11 The *Railway Times* 1839 p.442

12 *Guide de Duplessy* – 1840

13 *Jean-Baptiste Vifquain – Ingenieur, Architecte, Urbaniste (1789–1854)* Musée de Louvain-la-Neuve 1982

14 de Mijlpaal, Mechlin

15 Musée de Louvain op.cit.

16 Patent No.2028 granted for 15 years – Cabry's address at this time is given as Faubourg de Laken 4, Brussels

17 J. B. Masui, directeur des chemins de fer, *Musee de L'Industrie – Bulletin II – 1842.* 'Locomotives éxpansion variable, systéme Cabry'. 28 Octobre 1842

18 PRO RAIL 1008/18 letter dated 13 March 1842

19 PRO RAIL 1149/6 I. K. Brunel letter books, Folio 142. Letter Brunel to D. Gooch 28 October 1840

20 PRO RAIL 1149/7 I. K. Brunel letter books, p.218. Letter Brunel to D. Gooch 24 January 1843
21 de Mijlpaal – Staatsblad 17 August 1843
22 *Musée de L'Industrie – Bulletin-II-1842* op.cit.
23 Félia Mathias, *Etude sur les Machines-locomotives.* 1844
24 27 April 1844 p.32
25 *The Practical Mechanic's Journal* July 1846 p.279
26 14 January 1843 p.40
27 D. L. Bradley, *Locomotives of the South Eastern Railway 1st Edition.* RCTS 1963
28 J. Bek, *Historické Locomotivy.* Kadas, Prague 1978
29 8 June 1844 p.175
30 Patent for his 'Horse-leg' motion of 26 July 1838
31 *Musee de L'Industrie – Bulletin-II-1842* op.cit.
32 Manuscript transcript of Arbitration hearing held at the Law Institution at IME (Cabry's evidence given on 6 Nov. 1851)
33 These were consulted by D. L. Bradley (see note 27) and G. Dow, *Great Central.* Locomotive Publishing Company 1959
34 At some time prior to the 1968 Transport Act which required that such material be offered to the National Railway Museum for preservation
35 At the Science Museum Library
36 D. L. Bradley. op.cit.
37 Ibid.

38 The *Locomotive Magazine* 15 December 1925 p.393 and a letter in the issue of 15 September 1949 p.144
39 J. Goussens. *Egide Walschaerts 1820–1901.* de Mijlpaal Mechlin Belgium 1984 p.60
40 Robert Young, *Timothy Hackworth and the Locomotive.* 1923 pp.321, 406
41 Edward Dobson, *The Railways of Belgium.* John Weale 1843
42 W. J. Curtis. *Inventions for Railways …* London 1841
43 F. Whishaw. *The Railways of Great Britain & Ireland.* 2nd edition. John Weale. London 1842 p.268
44 Christopher Swan. *Cable Car.* Ten Speed Press, Berkeley, California 1978
45 J. C. Robinson. *Tramways; with a description of the wire cable system.* Edinburgh 1883
46 *Birmingham Central Tramways.* (Reprinted from newspapers) Birmingham 1886
47 A. Home-Morton. *The Glasgow District Subway: its construction, plant and working.* Glasgow 1897
48 S. C. Brees, *Railway Practice – 4th Series.* 1847
49 The *Railway Chronicle* 16 November 1844 p.825
50 Ibid. 5 October 1844 p.632
51 *PICE* Volume 10 1850/51 'Description of the mode of working the incline of 1 in 27½ on the Oldham Branch of the Lancashire & Yorkshire Railway'

52 The *Railway Gazette* 28 Feb. 1936 p.420
53 C. E. Stretton, *The history of the Midland Railway.* London 1901
54 F. S. Williams, *The Midland Railway, it's rise and progress.* 1876 p.91
55 Stretton, op.cit
56 PRO RAIL 371/41 Set of copy blueprints of early Liverpool & Manchester Railway locomotives, presented by C. E. Stretton
57 C. R. Clinker. *The Leicester & Swannington Railway.* Avon-Anglia Publications 1977 p.16
58 Ibid. p.72
59 *The Organ* Volume LV 1976/77 pp.74–84, where the alternative spelling 'Burkitt' is used
60 *The Tyne Mercury* June 1838.
61 *The Organ* Volume LV 1976/77 pp.74–84
62 J. W. Knowles 'Records of the musicians and musical services in York Minster, with notes thereon'. Manuscript in York Minster Library
63 PRO RAIL 1008/18 letter dated 13th March 1842
64 Whishaw. op.cit
65 The *Railway Chronicle* 1844 pp.755 & 989
66 Ibid.
67 E. F. Clark *George Parker Bidder, The Calculating Boy.* KSL Publications, Bedford 1983
68 Algemeen Rijkarschief, Brussels
69 The *Engineer* 21 December 1906 p.620

INDEX